Katherine had married Luis de Freitas because he needed her money—at least, she thought he did; but, once married, she realised he had been deceiving her all along. And that wasn't the only way he was deceiving her!

CAPTURE A STRANGER

BY

LILIAN PEAKE

MILLS & BOON LIMITED
15-16 BROOK'S MEWS
LONDON W1A 1DR

First published 1981
Australian copyright 1981
Philippine copyright 1981
This edition 1981

© Lilian Peake 1981

ISBN 0 263 73684 9

Set in Monophoto Baskerville 10 on 11 pt.

Made and printed in Great Britain by
Richard Clay (The Chaucer Press) Ltd,
Bungay, Suffolk

CHAPTER ONE

'I HOPE you'll agree at least to meet the man,' Katherine's father urged. 'He's not just any man, he's my sister Olga's stepson.'

'Let me think,' Katherine considered with a smile, 'was he the son of her third or her second husband? I've lost count.'

'Second, dear,' her father laughed. 'Now she's widowed again, but knowing her there's always time for another, even though she is nine years older than I am.'

'Her stepson,' Katherine mused. 'Does that make him some kind of relative?'

'Not at all. Certainly no blood-tie. How could there be? His father was Portuguese and left his native Madeira to come to Britain to "make his fortune", as the saying goes.'

'And did he?'

'He did, and he deserved to. He worked night and day. He saved hard, then married Mary—Mary Simmonds— in London. Their son Luis was born here. They took him back to Madeira as a child.'

'They took him—plus the "fortune"?' Katherine asked.

'It may not have been a fortune,' her father answered, 'but it was sufficient for Pedro de Freitas, Luis's father, to set up his own business there and prosper.'

'Are you sure, Dad, this man Luis isn't yet another of those rich men you keep introducing me to, hoping I'll fall desperately in love and thus marry into the "background to which I've been accustomed"?'

By her father's rising colour, it seemed she was in danger of rousing him to anger. She added hurriedly, 'Don't think

I haven't appreciated all you've done for me, but—well, I've had it *too* good all my life, and——'

'You wanted to break away. I've heard it all before.' He was staring inward and backward to the past. His thoughts were plainly not happy ones. He glanced around him and shook his head. 'When I look at how you're living, the place you've chosen——'

'I told you, Dad,' Katherine interrupted, 'I want to make a life of my own and live how I want. After all, I'm twenty-four now.' She was sitting on the floor and gazing up at her father. 'I wish you could understand.'

'I try to, my dear, I try, but——' he looked around again vaguely, like a man searching for a drink that wasn't there. 'I can't forget the years I lived in poverty as a child and the way my mother slaved to keep the family clean and well fed, while my father nearly killed himself working all hours to keep a roof over us. Yet here you are,' he motioned to the shabby armchairs, faded decorations, the unshaded light bulb, '*choosing* poverty when at home there's every luxury you could wish for at your fingertips.'

Katherine shrugged and stared unseeingly at her father's highly-polished shoes. 'Sorry, Dad, but that's the way it is.'

'You could have everything money can buy, Kate.' His use of her nickname moved her, but she still shook her head.

'I know you're going to tell me how you worked all hours in your turn, amassing a near-fortune so you could give—give me,' she dared not mention her mother, 'the luxuries and security you never had as a child.'

Halmar Matthews walked slowly to the window which overlooked the neglected garden. 'Much good it did me,' he said bitterly. 'It's driven you away just like it drove away your mother. You're two of a kind, aren't you?' There was a pause. 'All right, tell me what I know. I neglected her, yet I did it for her—for *her*.' It took him a moment to calm himself. 'She was so grateful to me she found another man,' he added bitterly.

Katherine closed her eyes, remembering how her father had agonised his way through the divorce proceedings. 'She's free again, Dad,' she reminded him gently. 'You know that Ronald has died?'

He did not seem to hear, but his back, normally straight, sagged a little.

Speaking lightly to lift the blanket of sadness from his eyes, she said, 'I think you're wonderful, Dad, and great and good, and I love you for all you've given me, but——' she rubbed at a worn place on the hearthrug beneath her, 'well, I just want to prove myself as a person—like you did but in a different way. I want to prove, not just to the world, but to myself, that I'm an *individual*.'

He turned and walked back. 'Just like your mother.' Katherine lifted her head and gave him an uncertain smile. 'Do you two have to look so alike?'

So, Katherine reflected, seven years haven't been long enough to assuage the wound my mother's desertion inflicted on him. Nor on me, she thought fiercely, for a fleeting moment feeling again like a bereft child. Maybe she had been all of seventeen when her mother had gone, but it had still hurt immeasurably. And it had been her father, the child in her accused, who had driven her mother away, her father's devotion to his work and, greatest irony of all, her father's success in that work, which had driven herself away, too.

'Dad.' She scrambled up, dusting the seat of her jeans free of coal dust from the open fire she lit in the grate most days. 'About Aunt Olga's stepson.'

'You'll see him, then? Good.' Again that vague look round, as if he were searching for a table on which to place his non-existent glass. 'He needs this money——'

'So he really is different from all the rest?' Katherine

frowned. 'If he's so desperate for cash, Dad, why can't *you* lend it to him?'

'Me?' Her father shook his head. 'It would be the company's money, dear, not mine. It's just not possible, even though I am the company's Chief Executive.' He smiled, more cheerful now, his florid features telling of expense account lunches with potential customers of the goods his sports equipment factories produced. 'Anyway,' he added, 'I'm doing you a service, easing that ridiculous conscience of yours, by presenting you with someone in need. You can lend him some of that large amount of money my sister Eleanor left you.'

'Aunt Eleanor should have known better,' Katherine answered with mock severity. Then she smiled. 'But she had a heart of gold. Like you, Dad.' She grinned at her father.

He grinned back, straightening his jacket again. His unhappy mood had passed. 'Nice-looking fellow, Kate.' He looked at her slyly. 'If you won't take a rich man for a husband, you might as well take a good-looker instead.'

'You're nothing but a matchmaker!'

'Call me a romantic, love. It sounds better. Well, I'll be going.' He started walking, then stopped. 'Olga will come with him, I expect.'

'So he needs his stepmother to hold his hand?'

'Hardly.' Halmar Matthews looked shocked, then he laughed. 'Wait until you see him, dear, that's all I can say. Then you can have the pleasure of playing the Lady Bountiful——'

'That's a role I'll never play!'

'My, you look fierce, Kate.' He used her nickname again, which brought a smile to her face, as he had known it would. He went to the door. 'I'll tell Olga you'll be pleased to see her—and her stepson.' With a smile, he waved and walked down the path to his car.

Katherine went into her bedroom, which was the front

room on the ground floor. Like the tenant upstairs—a solitary young man who appeared to prefer his own company—she had rented the flat from a couple who lived in a large house on the outskirts of London. Every month, in advance, she collected the young man's rent, then, together with her own, she mailed it to the landlord.

The place was adequately furnished, but she had added a rather scratched dining-table, two or three second-hand chairs, a bedside cabinet and a bookcase. The curtains had been bought by her from a jumble sale; her crockery and cutlery had come from the same source. Her father had said dismissively that she was playing at being poor, to which she had replied, if this was 'playing at it', then she'd hate to have to endure the stark, real thing!

'And if you say much more,' she had admonished him, 'I'll cut myself out of your will!' At which statement he had laughed himself breathless.

The following day, Olga de Freitas swept up the garden path, leaving her stepson to settle the taxi fare. Katherine, watching from behind the net curtains, assumed that her aunt had given him the money in the first place.

When the bell jangled, Katherine was at the door to open it. Curiosity about the stranger lifted her eyes for a fleeting moment over Aunt Olga's short figure. Brown eyes met hers and regarded her as closely as hers regarded him. Something in his glance made her heart spin and topple. This, of all men, must surely be the one she had been looking for!

What he thought of her it was impossible to tell, since the dazzling mixture of colours her aunt was wearing temporarily blinded her. She recalled her father's past references to his sister's love of the ostentatious.

As she hugged her aunt even before she entered the house, Katherine's eyes were drawn again past the pearl necklace which adorned the slightly crinkled neck to the tall, lean figure of the man standing just behind his step-mother.

'Katherine, my dear!' Aunt Olga stepped into the back room which Katherine used as a combined dining and living room. 'I'm so sorry to see you living in such—such surroundings!'

'Weren't you about to say "squalor", Aunt?' Katherine asked, her eyes twinkling. 'Don't worry, I haven't been banished to this by my hard-hearted father. He's as scandalised as you are. I chose this kind of life,' she added simply, 'because it's honestly what I want.'

Katherine did her best to avoid the eyes of the man who waited politely, while his stepmother placed her comfortable form on an upright chair, having refused the wooden-armed fireside chair her niece offered her.

'With your background, child,' Aunt Olga rebuked, 'I just cannot believe you're able to adjust to this.' Her horrified, roving eyes said the rest.

'I can and I have, Aunt,' Katherine assured her. 'I occupy the downstairs rooms. Upstairs, there's a shy, very quiet young man who's reading for an economics degree at London University.'

'You surely don't live in a house alone with a man!'

Katherine laughed at her aunt's exaggerated reaction. 'Aunt Olga, he's so immersed in his own life, I've hardly exchanged a word with him.' She smiled at her aunt's relief.

It occurred to Katherine that, as hostess, she could no longer ignore her other visitor's existence. Seeking his face with a strange and inexplicable shyness, the smile she sent his way was tentative and wondering. It widened her already large hazel eyes and parted slightly her well-defined lips.

Olga followed her gaze, exclaiming, 'Of course! I've been so astounded by the conditions in which we've found you, I've almost forgotten to introduce you to my stepson, Luis. I think of him as my son,' the man smiled at her with

something like affection, 'and I'm as fond of him as his
father, Pedro, was.'

The man spoke and Katherine found the deep timbre
of his voice immensely pleasing. 'You look puzzled, Miss
Matthews,' Luis de Freitas said.

'Your—your father was Portuguese, wasn't he?' Katherine queried.

Luis nodded. 'And I'm so English, is that it?' His flashing smile made her heart leap.

'Well, of course he is,' Aunt Olga broke in. 'He was
born here. He was named Luis Pedro Horacio de
Freitas—Pedro after his father, whom I married, Horacio
after his uncle, Pedro's brother.' Olga sighed. 'Pedro—he
was so proud of his son. "I'll leave my business to him,
Olga," he would say. "I shall have no hesitation in doing
so, because I know he will succeed. I have left you everything else." He kissed me then, and I thanked him in my
own way.'

'I remember how sad we all were to hear of your loss,
Aunt Olga,' Katherine sympathised. 'It was about a year
ago, wasn't it?'

Olga nodded, closing her eyes. 'We weren't to know
how short a time after that little discussion we would have
together. It was just as he'd told me. He left Luis the
business, which meant so much to him for so many years.
He also left me well provided for.'

Which, Katherine calculated, explains Aunt Olga's
expensive perfume and the gold rings she wears on the
four fingers of both hands. Any one of them, she estimated,
might well, if sold, produce at least some of the money
her stepson seemed to need so badly.

Once again her eyes bounced off his. My father was
right, she thought, about the good looks. Although 'good'
was hardly sufficient to describe the straight, determined
nose, the square chin with its cleft hinting at obstinacy,
the deeply brown eyes and the thick black hair.

The rest of him enhanced those looks. His physique was lean and tough, his arms which, at that moment, were folded as his shoulder rested against the high mantelpiece looked strong enough almost to lift a car. For a man who needed money as much as this man apparently did, she argued silently, he had no right to be looking at her so arrogantly.

The tilt of his head should have been less confident, his expression less quizzical. His eyes should not have been hooded and watchful. The breadth and strength of his shoulders should not have been so evident. Nor, she reproached herself, should the mere act of looking at the man disturb her so much.

The smile that touched his lips revealed that her scrutiny was amusing him. Anxious to borrow money he might be, she thought, but the aura of affluence still hung about him, left over, she reasoned from his father's financial successes. His clothes were casual, the open-necked shirt contrasting well with the brown jacket and slacks whose well-fitting cut could not be overlooked since the muscularity of his legs could be traced beneath them.

Katherine commented, to break the silence, 'So you were left your father's business, Mr de Freitas?'

'Make it Luis, please.' If his smile had not been so disarming, the tone could have been interpreted as imperious. For the same reason, Katherine's heart started beating faster. Annoyed with herself for showing such interest in the man, she attempted to subdue it by telling herself that since it was her money he was after, it was necessary for him to make a good impression.

She knew she should really dislike the man for coming to her, cap-in-hand, but how could she stop the female in her from searching for and being ensnared by the male in him?

'I was left my father's business,' he answered evenly.

'But you didn't succeed in running it as well as your

father thought you would?' Katherine had had no intention of taunting him, but by the curious flicker in his eyes
it seemed to her surprise that she had.

Olga's ample form seemed, to Katherine's dismay, to
wilt and sag. Answering for her stepson, she said, 'He
tried, dear, he did his best, but against enormous odds.
You see, we discovered Pedro's business wasn't as successful as he'd led us to believe. He kept assuring me everything was fine, but only he and his accountant knew the
real state of affairs. Not even Luis knew, did you?'

'Not even I knew, Mother.' He glanced at Katherine
and caught the puzzlement in her expression at his abrupt
tone of voice. Maybe, she reasoned, having to make such
an admission in front of her upset him.

Olga went on, 'Right from the start, Luis told his father
he had no interest in management. There are so many
stresses and strains connected with that level these days.
Don't you agree, dear?'

Remembering how her parents' marriage had been
ruined as a result of her father's devotion to his work,
Katherine nodded vigorously.

'I do understand.' She directed her words at Luis, but
her understanding seemed to leave him unmoved. She
cleared her throat. 'Well, I have this money Aunt Eleanor
left me. It's a very large amount, Aunt Olga.'

'Yes, dear.' Katherine was a little taken aback by her
aunt's fast switch back to her usual bright smile. 'My
sister—your father's sister, too, remember—usually played
her cards right in the marriage stakes. "If a man has no
money," she used to say, "he's not worth the ground he
stands on."'

Katherine laughed and she felt Luis's enigmatic eyes
on her. 'I happen to take the opposite view,' she announced. There was a swift flick upwards of his eyebrows.
Katherine challenged, 'If you don't believe me, Mr—or
should I call you *Senhor*?'

'For heaven's sake,' he returned irritably, 'I said make it Luis.'

'Yes, dear,' Aunt Olga confirmed comfortably, 'make it Luis. It's more friendly, don't you think?'

Katherine swallowed her irritation. 'Luis——' He nodded as she spoke his name. 'If you don't believe what I said about not disliking a man who hasn't any money, then why am I standing here offering to lend you as much as you need?'

'Maybe—family ties?'

She shook her head. 'Nothing like that, Mr—I mean, Luis. It's inner conviction, in accordance with my principles.'

He changed his position, straightening and slipping his hands into his pockets. Involuntarily, her glance went to his strong-boned hips.

The man's masculinity was magnetic, Katherine thought, annoyed with herself for not being immune to it. Yet why should she be immune? she asked herself.

Despite this man's tendency to display arrogance, he was not the usual kind of man her father was constantly urging her to marry. Not only was he good-looking, he needed money. Having no doubt been as over-indulged as she herself had been by a father's generosity, he was now seeing life from the other end of the scale. She decided that she liked him the better for it.

'Anyway,' she asserted, 'inner convictions or not, since it's my money you're asking for, I want to make sure it will be used wisely. It's only natural, isn't it?' A hint of a plea had, to her annoyance, entered her voice.

'But of course.'

Katherine gazed at him intently, trying to discern any veiled sarcasm, but his answering gaze seemed bland and entirely sincere. It irritated her that he was, or so it seemed to her, a past master in the art of inscrutability. This man might be in need of financial help, but she could sense that deep inside him there was a personality which might at times be daunting.

Attempting to show that she possessed some business sense, she challenged, 'If your father's business is in such a bad way, why can't you discover what went wrong? Then you could start to put it right.'

'Katherine, my dear,' Aunt Olga rose, brushing invisible creases from the brilliantly coloured skirt of her dress, 'if you're going to talk business, then I shall go. Luis, please call a taxi to take me back to the hotel.'

He nodded, then asked, 'If you would tell me, Katherine, where I might find your telephone—?'

The sound of her name on his lips caused a shiver to course through her. She told herself fiercely to be sensible, then at once asked herself, Why should I be? Her father's words came back to her. *If you won't take a rich man for a husband, you might as well take a good-looker instead.*

Katherine directed him to the hall, adding that the telephone was on the floor, since there wasn't a table to put it on. It was then that an idea came to her which made her spirits rise like a thermometer-reading in a sudden heatwave. If she could find the courage to carry it through, it would stop her father's matchmaking tactics for ever.

While Luis was absent, she made herself talk small talk to her aunt. Although she heard Olga's words and answered them, her mind was functioning on a very different plane. At that moment, she did not question why she felt so pleased with herself, nor why her pulse rate seemed to have increased alarmingly, but the man coming in from the hall undoubtedly had something to do with it.

After seeing his stepmother to the cab, Luis returned, his stride along the garden path firm, his muscle movements fluid and supple. There was a restrained sensuality about his body structure which had Katherine catching her breath. If there really was such a thing as love at first meeting, then it was surely happening to her.

Afraid that he would see the brightness in her eyes, she turned away. There was something else, too. He did not know it, but she had him, his future—and hers—in the palm of her hand.

'Katherine?' There was a caress in the word so subtle it had her turning to discover why. Was he trying to charm her into lending the money? Something in her rebelled at the thought that he could be so devious and she chased the idea away.

The brown eyes smiled as fascinatingly as the wide mouth. There was the warmth of the sun in his expression and it invited as surely as the lavish words in a brochure telling of the pleasures of sun-drenched lands.

The charm had already begun to affect her reflexes. The effort required to force her common sense to come to the rescue before she fell headlong into a tangle of emotional feeling for this man was already formidable.

Disciplining her wilful imagination—she had even begun to wonder what it might feel like to be in his arms—she told herself that the softening of his manner might, after all, be a prelude to pressurising her to make him a sizeable loan.

'Yes, Luis?' she asked, genuinely wondering what his objective might be. Her smile matched his, and her heart spun again, but he made no move to lessen the distance between them.

The fact that this disappointed her made her faintly irritable, telling her that although he might be appealing for her help and she the one with the power to say 'yes' or 'no', it was he who was in command of the situation.

'You're beautiful, Katherine.'

This, she told herself, was holiday brochure talk again, but she answered with all the ingenuity she could muster. '*Am* I?'

'You know damned well you are.' There was a glint in

his eyes now which had her muscles tensing. Instinct told her this was no ordinary man she was dealing with. Cold reason told her that his 'difference' stemmed from inheritance of temperament from his father's side of the family. This she *had* to believe, she urged herself.

He urgently wanted money, which meant he knew the meaning of need. Which also meant, she calculated, that he was on her side of society's fence—or rather, the side she had chosen for herself. Therefore, she continued reasoning, no barrier of outlook existed between them which had divided her from all the other men her father had hopefully introduced to her.

'The shape of your face is like a heart.' The message in his smile changed very slightly. 'Is it the only heart you have, Katherine? Or is there another beneath your breasts?' His eyes lingered lazily on the part of her to which he had referred.

His tactics were new, the sudden intimacy of his words disconcerting. She felt as if he had touched her, and cursed the giveaway colour. *Like a newly-blossomed rose.* The phrase was in her mind, but she expected that, at any moment, he would put it into words. He did not, and she looked at him, surprised. 'You've missed your cue,' she reproached.

When he threw back his head in laughter, his teeth gleaming white, the sight of the firm column of his neck and the flash of fire in his eyes, struck chords within her that made her wish fervently that she could still their vibration with her hands.

For all of her life, until that moment, her emotions had been under her own control. A shaft of insight, illuminated by the entirely unexpected intensity of feeling within her which this vigorously alive man in front of her had caused, told her that this was no longer true. There was the driving need, coming from her depths, to attack the person who had reversed her triumph and now held her, and her future happiness, in the palm of *his* hand.

'Why couldn't you save the business you inherited from your father by your own efforts?' she queried belligerently.

The question, she acknowledged, was really unjustified, in view of all that her aunt had told her. But he must have missed the unfairness of it, because the fire in his eyes did not die, nor did it turn into the crackle of anger.

'You know nothing about business, Katherine.' Again her spine tingled as he spoke her name. 'There are the employees to consider. Without them, there would be no goods to trade with.'

'What kind of goods?' she asked.

'In Madeira, there are a number of industries, more small than large. My father started an export company there with the money he had earned while living and working here. It flourished and expanded and, as we thought, was still expanding right until the day he died. Only my father's accountants knew the truth.'

'And it's for this company you want my money?'

'It is.' He held her gaze steadily.

'Has it suffered much from neglect?'

He paused, as if weighing every word. 'The working people have to be paid, Katherine,' he said at last.

'Are you telling me that mismanagement has brought your employees to starvation level?'

A faint smile crinkled his eyes. 'You're very concerned about the health of my employees, but I didn't mention the word "starvation".'

'Of course I'm concerned.' There was, she decided, a great deal he was not saying, possibly because it was too bad to talk about to her. She turned away, turned back, opened her mouth to speak, closed it again. Then, before her courage failed her, and because the man attracted her more than any man she had ever met, she put her proposition.

'I'll lend you the money, Luis, but on one condition.'

Katherine could have sworn he smiled, but it was so fleeting it had gone before she could be sure. A deep breath, she discovered, was needed to steady her heartbeats, since her lungs seemed unaccountably to be starved of air. She said quickly,

'On condition that you marry me.'

CHAPTER TWO

Luis's only response was a thrusting movement of his jaw. His expression was again inscrutable and, worst of all, unmoved.

Embarrassment put Katherine on the defensive. 'Am I such a bad bargain?' she demanded. She began to have a terrible feeling that she had made an unforgivable error of judgment. To her annoyance, her voice wavered. 'You told me just now I was beautiful, that my face was heart-shaped ...'

Comments, she told herself fiercely, not praise. What other compliments had he paid? None, she remembered. They had all been in his voice and in his eyes. Give up, she urged herself; it will only lead to humiliation. Yet something drove her on.

'My—my father has done his best to marry me to a rich man. He's introduced so many to me I've lost count. I hated them all. My father is wealthy, which made me, as they thought, right for them. They wanted to marry a woman in their own social stratum.'

His lean body relaxed. He leaned on his elbow against the mantelpiece. His face told her nothing.

Earnestly, she persisted. 'You see, Luis,' his eyelids flickered as she spoke his name, 'I wasn't really in their social layer. Money-wise, I was, but in my mind and my ideals, I'm—well, I suppose I'm on the side of the "have-nots".'

'Which is, maybe, why you want to marry me?' The question came softly, both surprising and confusing her.

'No—I mean, yes, yes, of course.' Luis's eyebrows lifted, and she realised her answer had not been very well worded. 'There are lots of reasons why—why I made that condition.'

He looked interested, but said nothing.

She sat in the armchair, wishing he would sit in the other, but he remained standing. His eyes were busy investigating her clothes, the simple shirt-blouse she wore, the tight jeans, the gold hoop earrings which caught the light as her head moved. Looking for censure but finding instead masculine approval of her femininity, she continued,

'My father's world isn't mine, any more than it was my mother's. In the end, she couldn't take it. She found herself an ordinary man, not poor but certainly not rich. Most of all, he was satisfied with his lot in life. What he had, he'd had to work for.'

'So had your father.'

Her head lifted quickly, her eyes were over-bright. 'My father didn't know when to stop. The more money he made, the more he wanted. Still does.'

'You're very hard on your father. He happens to love you.'

'I know, I know.' Her words indicated gratitude but impatience. 'But don't you see, I had to get away. All that luxury—it was strangling me, killing my individuality. So I broke away from it all.' She glanced around the shabby room. 'My father says I'm playing, and like a child, I'll soon tire of it. But I won't.'

He seemed prepared to listen all day if necessary, an attitude which encouraged Katherine to continue. 'Why do you think I want to help you? Because you're not rich like the others were. You may have been when your father was alive, but not any more. You can't be, otherwise why would you be forced to come to me for financial help?'

'I came to you for a loan, not marriage.' He moved to stand in front of her, looking down at her bent head. 'You're a fast-working little baggage, aren't you? Or was "marriage" a substitute for "affair"?'

Her head came up, her hazel eyes sparking with red

lights. 'No, it was not! I don't have affairs.'

'So you really want to marry me. Which can only mean you're using me to escape from your father's efforts to persuade you to marry money.'

'I'm not using you. I made that condition because——'
She jerked to her feet, brushing past him and feeling her leg tingle at the contact. She stared through the glass door to the garden. It wouldn't open as the hinge had broken, so she had to content herself with looking out at untended plants.

'Because——?' Luis prompted, and she felt him standing behind her. He was not touching her but her skin crept as if he were.

How could she tell him about the effect he had on her; how she had known from the moment they had met that he was the one—the only one for her, no matter how many other men she might meet in the course of her life? She couldn't tell him it didn't matter that she had never seen him before. Something inside her was telling her insistently never to let him go. She had fallen in love with him and wanted him to make her his wife. *That* was why she wanted to marry him; no other reason.

'Was it because you weren't content with revelling in your power over me through the loan you've agreed to make to me? You just couldn't resist tightening the screw—or the rope around my neck, call it what you will—and tie me to you?' He ignored the vigorous shaking of her head. 'We only met this morning. You know nothing about me, except what you see and what you've heard me say. I know nothing about you, except what I've seen——' He stopped, seeming deliberately to check himself. Katherine tried again to read his expression, and he caught her shoulders, bringing her right round.

Her eyes roamed his face at the same moment as his eyes, with uninhibited appreciation, roamed her body. That's the difference between us, she thought dismally. I see him with a woman's longing to love and be loved, by him and him alone, while he sees me simply as another female with whom he could satisfy his desires.

'And what I've seen so far,' he added, 'holds great promise. But,' his smile was twisted, 'what I've heard hasn't exactly commended you to me.'

'For heaven's sake,' she twisted from him, 'what have I said? All my life I've been surrounded by plenty. I only had to ask and I was given. In the end, it sickened me. Sometimes I needed only to look at something in a shop window an extra few seconds, and minutes later it was in my arms.'

'Which is why you thought you only had to look at me with those big, beseeching eyes and I'd be in your arms?'

'Why do you keep twisting my words?'

The long lashes over his probing brown eyes fascinated her—until she caught his cynical look. 'You've made a psychological error. You forget a man has his pride. When I take myself a wife, *I* shall do the choosing. And the asking. I will not be blackmailed into marriage with you just because you're making me a loan.' He went towards the door. 'Keep your money!'

'Luis,' Katherine cried, 'you can have the money!' He did not stop. 'I'm not blackmailing you, Luis.' If he walked out now, she knew he would never return. As he opened the door, she grew desperate. 'Where are you going,' she jeered, altering her tactics, 'to see your stepmother and ask her what to do about a girl who's just thrown herself at you?'

He slammed the door and closed the gap between them. 'Little hellcat!' His arm snaked round her, his other hand clamped on to her forehead, pressing it back. Her head went, too, and she thought her neck would snap. Her hands caught at his shoulder blades, bunching his jacket for support. 'No,' she gasped, 'let me go! My back,' she moaned.

His hand moved round forcing her head up. His mouth hit hers, his teeth mauled her bottom lip, and his lips explored the taste of her, forcing her to take all he was giving in punishment.

Then she was free and nursing her swollen mouth with the back of her hand. Her large eyes brimmed as they reproached him. 'Why,' she asked him, 'why?'

'Next time you'll think twice before you taunt a man, not to mention treading over his self-esteem with hobnailed boots.'

Katherine shook her head, still covering her mouth. 'I said you could have my money. What more did you want?'

Luis ran a hand over his hair, then rested his palms on his hips. 'I have to take *you*, along with the money, don't I?'

'I wouldn't let you take me now, not if I were offered a fortune.'

'So we shall have a marriage in name, will we?' He lifted careless shoulders. 'Just as long as you don't object when I bring my mistresses to my bed.' His smile was sardonic. 'I'd push you out of it first, of course.'

'Why, you——' She looked around for something to throw, but he was in front of her seizing her wrist.

He pulled her round to face him. 'Now, on the condition that *I* have imposed, will you still take me for your husband?'

Her lips parted as she gazed up at him. His glance dropped to contemplate them, like a photographer taking an aerial photograph for later study. 'You mean,' she asked breathless with disbelief, 'separate bedrooms?'

'Oh no, never that.' His reflective smile revealed where his thoughts lay.

'Well, what do you mean? That I must agree to your bringing in your mistresses?'

He looked into her scandalised face. 'That possibility can't be ruled out. It would depend on how good a wife you made me.'

Katherine jerked free. Her cheeks were flushed, her breathing fast. 'So now I know. I'd have to behave like a street-woman to keep you. You may not be in the high income bracket, but you think like a rich man, don't you? And to judge by the way you're talking about your private life, it looks as if you act like one, too. I take back my offer. If you want to borrow money, ask my father.' She pushed back some stray strands of hair, making a commendable effort to inject scorn into her scanning gaze. 'To think I liked you on sight! Some people say you should judge by first impressions. Well, I did, but how wrong I was!'

Looking at the door, then at him, she said, 'Tell my aunt I'm sorry I couldn't help her wonderful step-son——'

In a stride he was in front of her, seizing her arms. His jaw moved again, this time in a gritting action. 'You can stop talking to me in that tone!'

'Why? Who do you think you are? A man with power? You're down to the last coin in your pocket. You must be, otherwise you wouldn't have come begging to me——'

She saw by the fire roaring in his eyes that she had goaded him too far. His kiss was a savaging of her already bruised mouth. The resentment his treatment of her aroused surfaced in a wild twisting and turning of her body. Her knee lifted in a jerking wish to inflict her own pain on him, but before she could succeed he pulled her closer, making her legs powerless to hurt him.

Her teeth sought his cheek to snap and bite. He fastened on her chin and imprisoned her mouth again. Her hands caught at his hair, pulling at it. Then his whole demeanour changed.

His head lifted and he watched as she struggled to get her breath. In those few seconds his taut limbs had loosened, bringing down the temperature between them.

His cool lips lowering to hers began to soothe away the pain caused by his own brutality. He found the gap between the buttons on her blouse, easing it wider. The nerves along her spine tingled acutely as his caressing hands brought her soft breasts to hardening life.

Luis smiled, and this time his eyes flared as if a candle burned behind them. His arms around her tightened and he said. 'That is how persuasive I can be when I want a woman to say yes.'

The statement was provocative, but she could not fight him now. Her palms found his neck, pushing up to his hair again, this time to rake through it gently. Even if I'd wanted to resist him, she thought hazily, I wouldn't have had the resolve. With each new touch of his hands and lips, his power over her increased.

'Now will you say yes, little hellcat?' he demanded, his lips moving against her ear.

Happiness bubbled and she pretended to prevaricate, knowing that this time she would not anger him. 'Say yes to what?' she asked, flicking mischief from her eyes into his.

'To sleeping with me. Sharing my bed, my possessions, my future. The rest of my life.' But not his love. Well, her love for him would have to make up for his lack of love for her.

Her forehead went to his chest. His heart drummed beneath its hardness. 'Yes, Luis, oh yes!' Her eyes held his. 'You're everything I've ever wanted in a man.'

During the week that followed, Katherine saw nothing of Luis. He had returned to Madeira. Now that he knew he had the financial backing he required, he had told her, it was necessary to take some positive action where his late father's company was concerned.

His vagueness, Katherine concluded, was due to the fact that he knew that, even if he had been more specific, she would not have understood. The business world in general, and his in particular, was to her an unknown quantity. She was glad of his understanding, although it meant that she was handing her money into a kind of void.

She trusted him, she told herself, more than she had ever trusted any other person. Whatever she may have said to him angrily about the falseness of her first impressions, she believed that they had been right. Luis was, as she had surmised at that first meeting, an upstanding, honourable man.

This was why she was giving him her money—anyway, she would soon be his wife, and if a wife-to-be didn't trust her man, then the marriage would be pointless, since it would have no foundation.

The day before their wedding, Luis returned. From his stepmother's house in an expensive part of London, he telephoned her.

'I'm surprised to find you in,' he said. 'Don't you work for your living?'

Katherine retorted, 'Was that meant as a joke or a criticism?'

'Have I discovered a sensitive spot in your hard, tough exterior, Miss Matthews?'

'You *are* being sarcastic—aren't you?'

A low laugh caressed her ear, and it was as if his lips had touched it. 'Do you think I have your father's attitude to your style of living? That since you don't have a job, you're only playing at poverty?'

Stiffly, she answered, 'It sounded like it. So,' she attacked, 'you didn't think I was serious when I told you I hated the rich life, my father's choice of life-style which he was trying to impose on me?'

'My love, I believed every word. But please don't take every comment I make about the way you live as a criticism. I'm soon going to join you in it, remember?'

Katherine grew warm inside as his voice softened. 'How could I forget? Luis, I do have a job, more than one, but I don't take money. I have this inheritance and that's

more than sufficient. I go round the schools taking re-
medial classes—teaching children of different ages to read.
Those, that is, who've fallen behind the others in their
own age group. I help with young children in play-groups
too.'

'So it's a real do-gooder I'm marrying.'

'Mr de Freitas, if you go on mocking me——'

'Who said I was mocking you?' Katherine did not know
how to answer. 'I'm coming to you,' Luis said. 'There's
something about this telephone that's driving a wedge
between us.'

'It wouldn't be that you've been seduced by my Aunt
Olga's expensive life-style in the country of her birth,
would it?' she asked, too sweetly. 'If so, forget it, forget
me, the wedding, everything . . .'

Her answer was the slamming down of his receiver.

Covering her face with shaking hands, she felt a moun-
tainous wave of tears snarl and curl to break inside her.
One sob escaped, then control took over and the wave
was frozen. It wouldn't swamp her now. She had reached
a decision. Her marriage to Luis could not take place.

When he faced her on the doorstep, her lips were trembling, but iron determination kept her emotions in check.
He entered and followed her stiffly-held figure into the
living-room.

'Don't I get even a welcome-back smile?' he asked,
teasingly.

Katherine swung round. 'It can't take place—our marriage, I mean. I've decided I can't marry you.' Why
wouldn't her lips stay still? she thought, compressing them
in her effort to control the physical manifestations of her
emotional turmoil.

Now Luis was there, handsome and tanned, in front of
her, she wanted to marry him more than ever. It would
be so easy to drift with events, going to her father's house
that night as planned, dressing in the morning with the

help of a friend, appearing for the ceremony the radiant, deeply-in-love bride.

The teasing light in his eyes died. 'Am I permitted to ask why?'

He had in the space of a few seconds, changed his personality. Instinctively she knew that this was no man to play with, to wind round her little finger—*to propose to*! Her only course was to withdraw the condition, leaving him free to walk out of her life as easily as he had walked into it. But she didn't want to withdraw, she didn't want to watch him walk away ...

His fingers were slipped into his waistband. He wore jeans and his shirt had been pushed in unevenly as though he had been in a rush after a shower. The half-buttoned shirt revealed dark hair; the rolled-up sleeves showed the muscles and springing hair on his arms.

'Why?' Katherine repeated his question, having to gather her wits from her scrutiny of his lean, attractive physique. 'Well, I—I only met you a week ago. I don't know you, do I? Not the real you. I can see you and touch you, but I'm sure there have been a whole line of women in your life who have looked at you and wanted— wanted——'

His jutting jaw made her falter and stop. 'And you've probably concluded I gave them—what they wanted. You can conclude what you like. It's a side of my life you won't be hearing about from me.'

'I told you I didn't know you.' Her voice had thickened and she was not sure why. Was it that his words had conjured up pictures in her mind which had stirred her to *jealousy*? And if she was jealous, what did it mean? That she loved him? If she did, was that so strange? Hadn't she known on sight that this was the man she had been waiting for ... The questions chased each other like players in a football game. 'A week,' she repeated, 'that's all I've known you, and you've been away for most of that.'

Anger thinned his lips, tautened his jaw. 'What the hell are you trying to say? You tagged the marriage condition on to the offer of a loan. I wanted the money, so I accepted you with it. There was no other alternative.'

'Do you have to be so brutally frank?' she flung at him. Her lips were trembling again, but she refused to let him discover how easily he could manipulate her emotions. 'I'm saying I can't marry you. Don't you see? I made a mistake in suggesting marriage.'

'I seem to remember I was the one, in the end, who did the proposing. You weren't exactly slow in accepting my offer.'

'Now I'm trying to tell you I was wrong. I couldn't marry a stranger, because that's what you are.'

Luis smiled, but his eyes stayed cool. 'You'd disappoint your father, let all the guests down, send back all the presents?' He shook his head. 'I don't think so.' For a long moment he looked at her, his eyes as they roved over her slender figure calculating and cold. 'You're marrying me tomorrow even if I have to carry you to the ceremony.'

At the door he said, 'Go to your father's this evening as planned. Do everything as planned. Do you hear me, Kate?'

Her heart leapt as she heard the way her pet name sounded on his lips. There was nothing she could do—nor wanted to do—but return his gaze and whisper, 'Yes.'

The wedding ceremony made them man and wife only eight days after their first meeting. It was either that, Luis had said, or they lived together until her father could make the elaborate arrangements he had craved.

Katherine had asked for simplicity and, by repeating Luis's words, had persuaded her father to let her have what she wanted. There was a reception and the few friends Katherine had liked from her old life had been invited. Luis's relatives, he had told Halmar, were too far away to travel at such short notice.

Aunt Olga was there, dressed elaborately but with surprising taste. Katherine's eyes softened as they rested on her mother across the room. Standing on tiptoe, Katherine whispered into Luis's ear that she just had to speak to her. His gaze followed hers and he nodded.

'Mother?' Elspeth Pearson turned from the modern painting she had been studying on the wall of her ex-husband's living-room. Facing her was a brilliant-eyed daughter, dressed in a white ankle-length gown. 'I'm so glad you could come to my wedding. I did think you might not, because of having to see Dad again.'

'Katherine, my love . . .' Her warm arms encircled her daughter. 'Nothing, no one could keep me away from the event so many mothers long for——'

'And dread?' Katherine interposed, laughing. 'But it's different with us, isn't it? You went away a long time ago and——' She could never tell her mother of the pain she had endured at hearing the final quarrel, the final threat put into practice, listening to the door slam and knowing it was the end of family life as she knew it.

'It just had to happen, dear,' said Elspeth, releasing her daughter. 'Now, about you.' She glanced at Luis, in the centre of the group of which her ex-husband was one. Both men's eyes were reaching out—Luis's to the daughter, Halmar's to the mother of the daughter. Elspeth's glance backed away like a damaged car from an accident. 'Your husband seems a fine man, a good man. But darling,' her hand rested on Katherine's arm, 'you've known him such a little time.'

'Time enough to know he's all I want in the man I intend to live with for the rest of my life.'

Katherine realised with dismay exactly what she had said and was about to apologise when her mother smiled, not at her but at someone beyond her.

'That, my beloved wife,' two hands settled on her shoulders and her own hands went at once to cover them, 'is something I shall hold you to until our dying day.'

'It was a secret, Luis,' Katherine responded, glancing over her shoulder into the brown eyes and smiling features of her new husband. 'You weren't supposed to hear.'

'Don't worry, Elspeth,' Luis addressed her mother. 'I shall cherish her more than myself. Why are you frowning, kitten?' His lips brushed her cheek and she shivered. 'I have your mother's permission to use her name. After all, your father's Halmar to me.'

'Yes, but—well, Dad is Dad. Mum's different.'

'Darling,' Elspeth protested, 'I'm still your parent. Or have I turned into a stranger now?'

'Never!' Katherine exclaimed. 'Sometimes, when I'm awake in the night, I still imagine you're here with Dad . . . Oh, let's change the subject,' at her mother's sad expression, 'I'm getting morbid on my wedding day. Luis, do something to stop me from saying things out loud which are my own private secrets.'

Luis laughed with Elspeth. 'My love, in an hour or two we'll be alone and——'

Katherine cursed the colour that flowed over her cheeks. 'That isn't what I meant,' she protested, amidst more laughter.

'Luis!' Halmar called across the room. 'A business colleague of mine would like to meet you.'

Katherine frowned, clinging to Luis's arm. 'Why is Dad trying to involve you in his business affairs?'

Luis answered a little abruptly. 'Who said he was?'

'Then why didn't he call the man a guest and not a business colleague? Luis,' an anxious frown puckered her brow, 'don't go. Stay here with me. Don't get mixed up with finance. Now we're married, you can have as much of my inheritance as you want.' If she had paused to ask herself why a feeling of foreboding was at that moment squeezing the air from her lungs, she would not have been able to guess at the answer.

'Luis, are you coming?' Halmar's imperious voice lifted over the chatter and laughter of the guests.

Luis took a quick kiss from his wife's taut lips and assured her that he would not be away long. She watched as he walked, his bearing proud, to greet the man standing beside her father. If I hadn't known differently, Katherine thought, I'd have placed him firmly in the chief executive's chair of a thriving company.

'Are you having a honeymoon, Katherine?' Her mother's voice dragged her thoughts back to pleasanter things.

Katherine nodded, changed her mind and shook her head. 'Not really. We're going back to my place—our place, now.'

'Does it have soft lights, thick carpets and sweet music from the best hi-fi equipment money can buy?' Elspeth was smiling, but Katherine felt her mother's cynical question like a dagger thrust.

'Mum, you should see it! The carpets are almost threadbare. The light bulb doesn't even have a shade. The bed's double, but you roll into the valley down the middle.'

'And Luis doesn't object?' Katherine shook her head. 'Why, darling,' her mother persisted, 'when your room here, plus its en suite bathroom, is standing empty, waiting for you?'

'That kind of life—in the end I couldn't take it, Mum.'

It seemed as if her mother was holding her breath. 'So like me, you got out?'

'I got out. It was stifling me, depriving me of my individuality. Don't say you blame me for breaking away when you did the same thing.'

'I thought you at least would stay with your father.' Elspeth's voice was strained. Katherine tried to discover any trace of feeling for her father in her mother's face, but only a mask was visible to her searching gaze.

'He's lonely, Mum,' she ventured.

'Don't even try to persuade me, dear. Nothing would make me go back to him. Look at your father.' It was as if she were talking to herself. 'He hasn't changed. He's every inch the prosperous business executive. He has tens of thousands in the bank, yet still he goes on and on, accumulating money.'

Katherine lifted her shoulders, not knowing what to say. Her eyes sought for Luis. He seemed to be engaged in earnest discussion with her father's business friend. She wished she could hear the conversation. Was Luis learning how to revive a failing company? With *her* money? The irony struck her then and she checked the joyless laugh that rose to her throat.

'Once,' her mother was saying, her eyes looking fixedly at nothing, 'we were poor. We lived in a house like yours, everything shabby, hardly a penny to our name, yet we were happy—Halmar, you and me.'

'Oh, Mum,' Katherine put her arms round her mother's neck, 'I'm so glad Luis isn't a rich man. I love him so much I couldn't stand it if he was ever as successful as Dad.' To her own surprise, tears filled her eyes. 'I'm sure we'll be happy. Wherever we live, whether it's here or in Madeira, we'll be happy. I just know we will!'

'I'm married to you now,' said Katherine, looking up into brown eyes which she tried in vain to read.

They were back at her house. In spite of its shabbiness, in her elated state it held the gold-drenched beauty of an island in the sun.

There was a fleck of gilt – not gold – in those brown eyes now. 'You make it sound as if you've achieved something really great, like scaling the world's highest mountain.'

They were standing close, but not touching. They had not yet changed from their wedding outfits. Confetti was sprinkled over their hair, clinging to the silky white of Katherine's dress, resting on the broad shoulders of Luis's expensive-looking suit jacket.

He was her mountain. He seemed distant and remote. It scared her to see lights like glinting snow in his gaze. She would conquer him, she vowed, and stand at the summit like all the famous climbers, waving an ice-pick and proclaiming their achievement to the world. Except that she was no mountain climber, wouldn't even know how to start. Did that mean she would never enjoy the view from the top—the feeling of conquest?

'You may not know it,' she answered, 'but I have. I've married a man my father approves of—but *I* chose you, *he* didn't. Like my mother, I broke away and married an ordinary guy.'

'So you look on me as "an ordinary guy"?'

'Don't you like the label?' She frowned, afraid for a moment but not knowing why. 'It's one reason why I married you, Luis.'

He folded his arms and watched, smiling faintly, but she waited in vain for a response.

'You know that, don't you? she persisted. 'I told you, I didn't want my father's offerings. Rich men?' She clicked her fingers. 'I don't give that for them. Look at me, Luis——'

'I can't keep my eyes off you,' he drawled, and her skin crawled at his tone. He moved and his fingers flicked two or three pieces of confetti from the swell of her breasts.

'I'm not the beautiful, jet-set, glamour-loving type,' she went on, boldly countering his indolent gaze. A smile was pulled out of the fading remnants of wedding-day radiance. 'Am I your usual taste in women, Mr de Freitas?'

'Not exactly, Mrs de Freitas. But does it matter, since I married you for convenience, for expedience—some might say, under duress.' He watched her angry flush and smiled, looking her over. 'You'll do, my love. After all, it's your money that's of paramount importance now, isn't it?'

'You've changed.' Her eyes registered consternation, disbelief. 'You're not the man I f——' She almost gave away her secret, that she loved him. Quickly she finished, 'The man I found standing on the doorstep.'

'Like a starving beggar holding out his hands?'

Katherine backed away, her eyes widening in alarm. 'Sarcastic, cynical—did you catch those afflictions in your younger days, when your father's wealth over-indulged you, like my father's did me? If so,' she choked, 'I don't want to know you—not in any sense of that word.' She tugged at the wedding ring. 'You can have this back.' To her fury it would not move. 'We'll have an annulment.'

Luis followed, taking his time. She felt behind her back for the door handle, fumbling without finding it. He said, swinging her away from the door and putting his own back to it, 'If you really believe I'd allow the catch of the season to slip through my fingers, then you're very much mistaken.' His hands closed tightly round her upper arms. 'Look at you—wide-spaced, inviting eyes, a mouth that's begging to be ravished, a chin which pushes itself out cheekily asking to be nipped. Oh no, my sweet wife, there'll be no annulment.'

Her arms lifted and jerked in her efforts to get away. 'I—I can prove non-consummation.' She coloured slightly at the information she had inadvertently given him.

He let her go at once. His expression was inscrutable, but his words held a strangely discordant note. 'You're trying to make me believe I've got myself a virgin bride? That I was handed on a plate a flawless diamond out of all the chipped, dulled imitations I've handled in the past?'

His voice grated and she put her hands over her ears.

He reached out and tugged at her wrists, holding them.

'It's true,' she declared, trying to break free. 'And I didn't "hand myself to you on a plate". I've never wanted a man before, never allowed—— '

'But you want me now?' His hold slackened, his thumbs caressed the inside of her wrists.

'I wanted the man you were before today. I don't want the man who's just become my husband. What's happened to you, Luis?' she asked, bewildered.

He ignored her appeal to his better nature. His eyes swept her shape, the way the dress followed it faithfully, the collar uplifted to frame her face. 'Untouched you may be, but that didn't stop you throwing yourself at me along with your money. You bought me, therefore I dance to your tune. Is that how the reasoning goes in that tiny brain of yours?'

'Any more insults?' she attacked, swallowing back the tears.

'Insults? The biggest insult was the one you aimed at me. With this loan I thee, my stud, the future father of my children, wed.'

'Your pride—I've hurt your male pride! Well,' she retaliated, 'I don't care a damn for your male pride. You can keep it, and your lovemaking, for some other woman. We may be married now, but,' she hesitated since she was about to tell the biggest untruth of her life, 'I wouldn't let you make love to me and t-take me now, not if you begged me to let you!'

His hands cupped his elbows and he looked down at her with slitted eyes. 'No? When I decide to do so, my little hellcat, there'll be no begging on my part. Be certain of one thing—I'll take you in my own good time.'

CHAPTER THREE

KATHERINE turned and twisted in her bed. For the first time, it seemed too large. Strange, her restless brain registered, how she had never been conscious of its size before.

Two hours now, two hours since she bathed and slipped into her filmy nightdress and slid beneath the covers, waiting, waiting. She had spent the evening waiting, too. When she had left Luis in anger, his harsh words stinging her ears, she had changed in the bedroom, taking off the white dress and wrapping it carefully in tissue paper. The box in which it had been delivered to her father's house and in which she had replaced it now lay flat on the floor of her cupboard.

Hopefully, she had dressed in jeans and shirt and gone into the living-room. Her intention was to make amends, to put her arms round her new husband's neck and whisper that she was sorry. The fact that he had done his share in inflaming the quarrel didn't matter any more. The fact was that she loved him and wanted to show him that love mattered more than any pride. It clamoured to be told—and demonstrated.

The room was empty. Her flat was empty. Luis had gone—where she did not know, could not guess. No use calling upstairs to the young man, Have you seen the man I came in with? He's my husband now. I married him today. Now I've lost him. Isn't that funny? No use, because the upstairs tenant had gone away.

The meal she had eaten was minimal. There was no food that she knew of which was made more appetising by swallowing it with tears. Not that she had cried. The tears were locked inside her and she had mislaid the key.

Still she listened—and kept on waiting. An hour later, her tension having deepened unbearably, she heard the front door opening. He must have taken the spare key which she had told him hung on a rack in the kitchen. Where had he been? *Where would he go?*

Quivering, she sat up and listened, her hearing keen, despite her fatigue. There was the sound of a bath running in. She subsided, head on pillow, eyes staring at the patch of light on the ceiling which crept between the door and the frame. The bathroom door creaked open. Luis seemed to be making for the living room.

A sigh of despair caught in her throat. So the rest of the night, her wedding night, she would have to spend alone. Where he would sleep, she did not know. Nor, she tried to convince herself, did she care.

It wasn't true. She sat up again. Her mind cared; her body cared; her conscience cared. It was through her own foolish machinations that Luis had married her. She had taken advantage of his plight, his financial need, and forced him into marriage. It was therefore wrong of her to deny him his rights as her husband. Besides—she scrambled out of bed and pulled on a wrap—she wanted him. *She loved him.*

Her door creaked as she opened it, but her bare feet made no sound on the cold, tiled floor of the hallway. She found him sprawled in an armchair, his feet lifted to rest on another chair. Except for his jacket, he wore his day-time clothes, but his tie had been dispensed with. His eyes were closed, but they flicked open at her quiet approach, showing that he had not been asleep.

There were shadows under his eyes, a dark area around his chin and upper lip. His arms were folded across his chest and he looked as though he was prepared to spend the rest of the night right where he was.

'Where have you been?' Katherine had intended it as an accusation, but the wavering note extracted its sting.

'At your father's place, exchanging tales of wife-rejection, something we both have experience of.' His words taunted, his eyes derided. She pulled the silky wrap more closely about her shivering figure. It was a garment left over from her richer past and it irked her that his jeering eyes had missed neither its quality nor its irrelevance to her present shabby background.

'Please leave my mother out of this,' she answered stiffly.

He roused himself, lowering his feet and moving to stand in front of her. His shirt hung loose, having been left unbuttoned after his bath, and Katherine's eyes were drawn to his lean body, treacherously giving away the feelings she most wanted to hide. His hand lifted her chin, and her heart pounded madly as the eyes of a stranger laughed mockingly into hers.

'Your father warned me to be wary, to treat you with caution,' he told her. 'If necessary, I should bind your hands and imprison you so that you couldn't get away. That was the only way, he told me, to treat the daughter of his ex-wife Elspeth. You're elusive, he said, both of you. Made of the same stuff, so high-principled it hurt, intolerant of others' weaknesses and completely without compassion.'

'My father—*my father* said that? I don't believe it. You're making it up.'

'No need for me to make it up. He said it all right. Why shouldn't he feel bad about the two of you? You both deserted him.'

With that there was no arguing. All the same, Katherine jerked her chin away. 'I've got *his* characteristics in me, as well as my mother's. So what does that make me?'

'An intriguing mixture. Highly combustible, too, I imagine. I'll handle that mixture with care. Well,' his glance raked her, 'what do you want with me? To act the tame and dutiful wife to me and consummate our marriage?' He grasped the wrap and pulled it open. His gaze darkened dangerously. 'No, there would be no "tame" about it if I mated with you tonight.'

Pulling the wrap around her, Katherine turned away. 'I was worried about you, that's all. I wondered where you'd gone.'

'Did you think I'd found consolation in the arms of another woman?' Luis jeered. 'Would you have cared if I had?'

Her large, tired eyes lit with anger. 'On our wedding night? I'd have hated you. Anyway, the idea that you might—do that to me never came into my head.'

'So, like a wife who has been married years instead of hours, you were honestly concerned about me. You were really worried.'

'Stop laughing at me!' Once more it was meant to be spoken in defiance, but again the quiver in her voice let her down. She went to the door. 'You can sleep where you like. Why should I care?'

He followed her along the hallway to her bedroom. 'I shall indeed sleep where I like.' His shoulder easily stopped the slamming door. 'And that is with you.'

Katherine tugged off her wrap and flung herself diagonally accross the bed, occupying as much of it as her slim body could manage. She pulled the covers tightly to her chin, closed her eyes and waited. The battle she had anticipated did not come. Her eyes flew open and she saw by his smile that he knew exactly how she felt. It also revealed to her a slightly devilish side to him she did not know— amongst all the other things about him she did not know.

His eyes gleamed in the light from the bedside lamp as he divested himself of his shirt, throwing it aside. When his hands went to his belt buckle, Katherine gasped, 'Luis, no!'

His hands rested there. His head threw a shadow over

his strong torso and the muscles in his arms reflected that same strength, warning the girl who gazed at him so warily to keep her temper or else ... Or else, his faint smile cautioned, she would be forced to take any punishment those arms and hands cared to mete out.

'Katherine, yes!' he tossed back mockingly, yet stood motionless. 'I am fully male, my love.' The endearment—was it sincere? She eased back the bedclothes and knelt up, searching his face thrown into shadow by the light from the bedside lamp. It told her nothing. His faint accent had become more pronounced, reminding her yet again that she had married a stranger.

His tone softened. 'I am also your husband. Do you find me so repelling you're afraid to look at me as nature made me? Or have you never seen a naked man before?'

If she told him that the mere thought of him "as nature made him" excited her so much that her heartbeats doubled their speed, his reaction would, she guessed, have been so swift, he would know of her secret love for him the moment he touched her.

Against all her clamouring instincts, she prevaricated. 'I—I've been around.' The moment she had spoken, she realised he would misinterpret the statement.

'Have you indeed?' he drawled, flicking his eyes over the shape of her beneath the transparent nightgown. 'So maybe I shall have a—surprise when I make you mine. Maybe I'll discover you have belonged to other men, too.' His hand moved and stroked her hip, covered though it was.

'I didn't mean it in that sense. Try to understand,' she pleaded. 'I want you to make love to me, to be my real husband, but——'

'But you're shy? My little hellcat has turned into a furry kitten and wants to be stroked and coaxed? You delight me, my own.' There wasn't, surely, an edge to his voice? Instinctively she began to withdraw into herself. He sensed it at once and encircled her kneeling figure with his arms. 'In the country of my birth, an untouched girl is sought after as a wife. Never did I believe that a girl from your way of life, who forced me to marry her, would have saved herself for me.'

Katherine tried to jerk away, but he held her more firmly. She had been right about the edginess. Would his wounded pride never heal? Her cheek turned to rest against his ribs and his heart was drumming almost as hard as her own. Her head went back and she looked again into his face.

There was one way which only a woman could know to soothe the rawness of that pride. Her arms reached up and fastened round his neck. What surprised her was the amount of pressure she had to use to bring his head down to her own level. Then she remembered that pride of his and his resistance told her how hard her fight would be to heal it.

Her mouth strained upwards and kissed his lips. They were hard and unyielding. She shivered as icy, invisible fingers played a discordant tune along the line of her spine. Her palms slipped over the broad, tanned shoulders, fingertips running over the hard column of his neck. Her eyes held his unfathomable gaze, then, with a small sound of near-despair, she ran her fingers through the thick blackness of his hair. Still there was no response.

A heavy sigh came from her and she sat back on her heels, looking helplessly up at him. The urge to shake him was overwhelming, but she knew it would be as useless as shaking an ancient tree, hoping the action would bring it down.

'Luis, please, please, I don't know——' She sighed again. 'I just don't know,' she finished flatly.

He had straightened and his arms were folded across his chest. In the half-light he looked like a slave-master, waiting for his slave to perform. His head was in shadow, now, and it angered her that she could not see his expression.

'For a girl who's "been around",' he quoted her words, 'you know surprisingly little about making love to a man.'

'But it's the man who makes love to the girl,' she exclaimed exasperatedly.

'Not this man to this girl.' His hand bunched under her chin, pushing it up roughly and letting it fall. 'Where are those claws, little cat? Sheathed now you've caught me? Or think you have.'

Her hands flew up towards his face. She could not reach it, so her nails ran down his chest, raking through the dark hair. Her wrists were trapped by equally clawing fingers. Eyes, nearer now, glinted brown and gold in the light from the shaded lamp. 'One thing you will do before I lay a hand on your body. I shall not tell you what that is.' He threw her wrists from him. She followed the path of his eyes back to herself, and knew what he meant.

At first she shook her head, reflecting the thought that told her she couldn't do it. Then her eyes appealed. 'You—you do it, Luis. Please....'

He did not move. There was, she knew, no alternative but to do as he had silently commanded. Her movements slowed by reluctance to do as he wanted, but most of all by shyness, she found the hem of her nightgown and started to lift it. She stopped, challenging him.

'Why should I? I've never been taught the tricks and techniques a woman uses when she wants——' she took a steadying breath, 'wants a reluctant man to—to seduce her.'

Luis stood away from the lamp's circle of light, so that she could not discover his mood or expression. 'Even if I were "reluctant", my own, which I am certainly not, your deliberate slowness would by now have made me crazy with desire.'

'Stop mocking me!' she responded violently. 'And my slowness is not deliberate. I just—can't—can't——'

'Turn from girl to enticing woman? Maybe this will help.' His hands found his belt yet again, and Katherine knew that telling him 'no' would not work a second time.

The sight of him, a handful of seconds later, standing tall and powerful, was potent indeed. It lit a fuse inside her which had the blood in her veins turning into a river of fire. Her fingers, shaking a little, slipped the gown from her shoulders. For a moment she let it rest where it had fallen on the bed, then she shook it away and swung to the floor, facing him.

'Now tell me you want me.' The words came from him tersely.

Her nakedness, dwarfed by his abounding masculinity, made her feel deeply vulnerable, but she overcame her instinct to cover herself again.

'Tell me you're mine.' The order came more sharply now and forced from her a small cry.

'I want you, Luis,' Her arms stretched towards him. 'I'm yours, I'm yours!'

It seemed an eternity before he moved. Even so, it was only a pace nearer. Katherine still could not read his eyes. 'Please, please,' she pleaded, 'I've done what you asked of me.' His lack of response maddened her into crying out his name.

Her feet carried her fast towards him and her arms clung to his hard, unbending body. The feel of him against her brought the nerves of her skin to stinging, feverish life. The rough hairs on his chest prickled her cheek and small sounds came from the back of her throat.

When he responded at last, it was like a volcano erupting. His arms lashed like rope around her, impressing her body on his. She could feel his desire, his strength, his indomitable, male demand. He carried her to the bed and together they dropped on to it.

He was on his side, caressing her, his hands and lips never still in their arousal, her responses driving her to twist and turn in an ecstasy she had never known. Over and over, she gasped his name, parting her lips for his kisses, giving herself to him so completely that when the moment came for them to become truly man and wife, she cried out in complete abandon,

'I love you, Luis, I love you with every single part of me.'

Later, they lay entwined, the covers over them, and slept.

In the morning Katherine awoke first. All night his arms had not left her, and as she moved to push a lock of his dark hair from his face, the feel of him against her began to revive the smouldering fires which contentment had dampened down.

Her finger running down his profile brought his eyes open and a smile to the lips which had snapped at her fingertips. 'My creditor seems pleased with the husband she has bought.'

Instant anger shot through her, making her struggle free and turn from him. He caught her shoulders, pulling her backwards. His mouth fastened, upside down, on to hers and although her arms and legs flailed, there was nothing she could do.

When he pulled her across him and his hands started playing havoc with the most vulnerable parts of her, her arms reached up and she succumbed, with urgency, to his freshly aroused demands.

Satiated, they lay, some time later, and she burrowed into him. 'I belong,' she murmured, 'I belong to you.' His mouth feathered the back of her neck and she lifted her head to find his brown eyes laughing at her. It was the amusement of indulgence and satisfaction, not mockery. She only wished she could have identified the emotion of love.

Not once had Luis used the word, not even lightly, not even to reassure her that he had married her for anything but to fulfil the condition she had imposed. It was like the merest scrap of cloud in her otherwise sun-gilded blue sky. Just as long as the cloud didn't grow, she thought, but stayed small and finally went altogether. And that, she told herself, would be the day he told her he loved her.

'How can I heal your wounded pride, darling?' she queried, rubbing her thumb over his stubbled chin and upper lip. 'Will you ever forgive me and yourself for accepting my loan?'

'Never,' he replied, rolling the word over his tongue, 'till the day I die.'

Katherine laughed, but secretly she wondered if his statement, spoken in amusement, had been seriously meant.

It was curiously intimate sharing the bathroom with her new husband. And unnerving, she discovered, every time they touched unexpectedly through the smallness of the room. While she washed and brushed her teeth, Luis shaved, using the inadequate mirror propped on the windowsill against her cosmetics. Later, Katherine decided, she would take a bath.

Even this she looked at with new eyes—Luis's eyes. It was rusting and stained from the constantly dripping tap. 'I'm sorry,' she said, speaking as a result of her thoughts. Luis looked startled and she explained, 'that the bath isn't very inviting.'

He laughed and discarded his razor. 'What did you have in mind, my love? That we should share it, here and now?'

Katherine coloured, hiding behind her towel. 'Of course not!' She peeped from its folds. 'You didn't mean it, of course.'

'I certainly did.' He reached out, but she backed away.

'I can see I have a great deal to teach my new wife.'

'We must eat,' she said, and ran from the bathroom, down the stairs to dress.

A week went by, seven days of undiluted happiness, of hand-holding in the street, of seeking out new eating places in London, then driving into the country. Nights of making love, hours of walking in sunlight, even on cloudy days, of walking on that cloud and forgetting the rest of the world existed.

Every time payment was called for, Katherine offered to give her money to Luis. He lifted a shoulder uncaringly. 'You do the paying. Stop worrying about my self-respect. It doesn't suffer just because you're the one to settle the bills before leaving or pay the taxi driver, adding extra for shutting his eyes to our embraces behind his back.'

Even as she paid, and paid again, for all they did, and even though Luis had unquestionably agreed to her doing so, she sensed that there was in his eyes the merest glimmer of something like resentment. He persisted, however, in refusing the money. Nor, she noticed, did he once offer to pay himself. This both surprised and, faintly, worried her.

It was all forgotten in the passion of their coming together in the dark hours of the night. The drabness of the house and the environs of the neighbourhood faded, becoming instead gilt-tinted by the hazy sunshine in her mind. Just to turn her head and find him beside her, walking or lying full-length; sharing with him the small kitchen and cooking their meals together, was to her the pinnacle of delight.

Nine days after their wedding, Luis said, 'Sweetheart, I have work to do.'

The bells that had been ringing so sweetly in her mind for the whole course of their passion-filled honeymoon grew into a frightening clangour. She wanted to cover her ears to keep out the sound, but her reason, functioning slowly as if from suspension of use, told her that such an action would only lock in the raucous noise.

Instead she shook her head with such vigour that her hair covered her eyes. His hand moved to push it aside. 'Life goes on,' he said softly, pulling her to him.

Even as he held her she could sense a change in him. 'The world's starting to intrude,' she muttered against his chest which his open-necked shirt revealed. 'Tell it to go away, Luis. It—it frightens me.'

He laughed, and she felt the reverberations beneath her cheek. It was like a warning of an approaching earth tremor and she gripped his shoulders in an instinctive gesture of self-preservation.

'Have I made you so happy,' he whispered, his lips against her ear, 'that you haven't noticed the world has never gone away?'

I made you happy? Katherine stiffened, considering his words. Why had he phrased the question that way? Shouldn't it have been, Have *we* been so happy . . .?

Her eyes searched his. 'Haven't I made you happy, too?'

'Deeply happy.' Not a trace of mockery could she find, but it sounded ominously like a kind of parting, as if they were being 'put asunder', whatever the marriage ceremony had dictated, not by man but by circumstances. What circumstances were they?

If only her mind would stop torturing her! If only it would accept the present, with the happiness it offered, and stop reaching out in a probing, robot-like action to dredge through the future.

They had washed the dishes. Luis took the dishmop from Katherine and placed it on the chipped enamel draining board. He freed her hands from the rubber gloves she wore to keep her hands smooth.

His gaze wandered over her radiant face. There was no questioning the admiration his brown eyes reflected, but it was mixed with something else—a kind of distraction, Katherine decided, as though his mind was torn in two. Part of it revealed the still-enchanted lover, and this she revelled in.

It was the other—preoccupied—part which played again that jangled tune in her head. He was with her, yet he was not.

'We must return to Madeira.' His words made the earth seem to rumble beneath her feet.

'When?' she asked, her mouth dry. He took a few moments to answer and it seemed to her that he was already there. She gripped his shoulders as if trying to hold his body back from following his mind's flight from her. 'Not yet,' she urged. 'Surely there's been someone in charge in your absence? I'll send him all the money you need. He could at least pay the employees....'

A flash of irritation darkened his eyes, then it was gone, leaving Katherine wondering if it had ever been. 'There's more to it than that.' His fingers gripped her arms and she knew she would discover bruises next day. At that moment, she felt numb in both mind and body.

When he let her go, his former irritation had returned. 'You must have known the time would come when you would have to come with me.'

'What—what kind of place is your home, Luis?'

He smiled briefly. 'It's not a primitive cave, if that's what you're hoping. Nor is it a wooden shed, nor even like this place.' He scanned her face. 'Why the frown? Did you think my way of living resembled the style in which you've chosen to live?'

'Well, I——'

'Can you really imagine my stepmother agreeing to share a house with me which had a rusting bathtub, peeling wallpaper—you know the rest,' he finished, looking round.

'Of course, Aunt Olga's house! Left to her by your father?'

'When my father returned to Madeira with the "fortune" he had earned abroad, he made a number of investments—property and so on, including the house he chose to live in with myself and my mother and later, when my mother died, his new wife—Olga.'

Katherine's eyes opened wide. 'So that's what Aunt Olga meant when she said your father had left her well provided for!'

Luis looked at her steadily.

'That's the house we shall live in?' Katherine asked. 'With Aunt Olga?'

'I believe she has other ideas.' He seemed unwilling to add to the statement. Probably, Katherine reasoned, because he simply didn't know of his stepmother's plans. His arms linked round her waist. 'How long will it take you to pack?'

'You mean we're going soon?'

'Two—three days, maybe. What will you do about this place?'

'Inform the landlady. Take my personal belongings and leave the rest. The odd pieces of furniture I bought myself can stay. The next tenant will probably appreciate them.'

'We shall have to tell your father.'

Impulsively Katherine suggested, 'Let's ring him at the office.' A few minutes later she was being told by his secretary that Mr Matthews was not in today. Frowning, she replaced the receiver. 'He must be at home.'

'Or a conference?' Luis suggested with a smile. 'A meeting? Or maybe travelled north—or south, or even abroad?'

Katherine laughed. 'You seem to know it all! How did you learn—through your father?'

'He wasn't quite that kind of businessman. When you come and live with me in Madeira you'll see what I mean.

All the same, he never stopped working, until the very end.'

Katherine smiled, then frowned uncertainly. 'If he was that kind of man, then how was it he left his financial affairs in such a mess?'

'My love,' Luis arm went round her, 'finance is a subject I refuse to talk about on our honeymoon. Let's go and see your father's housekeeper. Maybe she knows where he's gone.'

'I suppose,' Katherine sighed resignedly, 'we must emerge into the real world again.' She went to the door. 'I'll get changed.'

Katherine stood beside Luis on the doorstep of her father's large house. She had forgotten the key she still had in her possession and Luis had rung the bell. Bridget, the housekeeper, gave them a smiling welcome. 'Your father's home, Miss Katherine.'

'Thanks,' Katherine answered. 'In here?' She indicated the living-room, and the housekeeper nodded.

'Dad!' Katherine rushed forward to hug her father, who had risen from an armchair. It was the first time she had seen him since her wedding day.

'Let's look at you,' Halmar Matthews said. 'Is your husband treating you right? Hm, looks as though you're treading on air.' He looked up at his son-in-law. 'All's well, Luis?'

'All's well, Halmar.' There was an exchange of smiles between them.

'You see, Dad,' Katherine put her arm round Luis's waist, 'I made the right choice. What's more, I made it myself, without your help!'

'You certainly did,' Halmar answered, his eyes twinkling. 'And does he mind living in imitation poverty, sharing secondhand furniture and threadbare carpets with you?'

'I know you're only trying to rile me, Dad,' Katherine returned placidly.

'The bed's fine,' Luis interposed. He looked down at his wife, pulling her close. 'It has a hollow down the centre which is a kind of meeting place, if you know what I mean.'

'Good psychology,' Halmar commented. 'If you have a row and go to bed intending to lie back to back, you just roll to the centre and meet there.'

'Where an excellent reunion takes place,' Luis added, laughing at the tinge of colour in his wife's cheeks.

'We haven't had a single quarrel,' Katherine stated, looking up and meeting Luis's eyes.

'Well,' Halmar sat down, not without a touch of weariness, 'at least she hasn't left you—yet.'

'Leave him?' Katherine returned, her eyes full of protest. 'Never!'

'I'll hold you to that, my love.'

Halmar looked from his daughter to his new son-in-law, then looked away.

Katherine remembered and was immediately contrite. Her own mother.... Glancing at her father, she noticed his pale cheeks. 'Is something wrong, Dad?'

Halmar shook his head. 'Tired, that's all.'

'Tired? But it's Monday morning. You've had the week-end——' Halmar shook his head. 'You brought work home?' Her father nodded. 'You know that's the worst thing any man could do.'

'Tell me, my dear,' his head turned slowly, 'what else is there? When a man's alone.... I've realised, too late in life, the value of a constant and loving companion. And,' his hand reached out quickly to cover his daughter's as it rested on the arm of his chair, 'don't start thinking of "reunions" where I'm concerned, love. That would be wasting your time.'

'Mother? You asked her?'

'I asked her. And it was "no". What did you expect?'

Katherine could have wept at the hopeless note in her

father's voice. She could never do to a man what her mother had done, no matter what he did. And certainly she could never leave Luis. Her eyes followed her thoughts and she smiled up at him. He did not smile back.

'We're leaving for Madeira in a few days, Halmar,' Luis said, and there was a curious note of resolve in his voice.

'Do you mind, Dad?'

'Mind, my dear? How could I? You're a wife, then a daughter. Wife first, Kate, always first.' His voice had faded a little, as though in his thoughts he was far away.

Drinking the coffee which Bridget had carried in, Katherine arranged to bring her belongings to be stored in her old bedroom at her father's house. 'There won't be many,' she promised. 'I'll throw out as much as I can.'

'Knowing you,' her father joked, 'you'll throw very little away.' To Luis, he said, 'I've never known such a hoarder.'

'Of dreams,' said Katherine, smiling brightly into her husband's eyes.

'Dreams?' her father responded. 'Yes, hold on to those. Treasure them all your life. They may be all you have.'

CHAPTER FOUR

THEY were passing over the Bay of Biscay, the pilot announced. Katherine caught a glimpse of the coastline of France. Her head returned to Luis's shoulder, her arm through his arm.

He was reading through papers which, she supposed, were connected with the business his father had left him, the business which, she thought with a smile, she had helped to save.

Since the words were in Portuguese, Katherine could not understand them. Nor, at that moment, did she care. She tugged at Luis's arm for attention.

'How long is Aunt Olga staying in the Caribbean?' she asked, running a finger over the dark, fine hairs on the long, masculine hand which held a pen.

'With Olga, one never knows. Why?' Luis's eyes did not stray from the papers.

'I just wondered how long we would be alone together at your house.' She peeped shyly into Luis's face and found him smiling to himself. He made no reply and Katherine went on, 'What's Aunt Olga's house like?'

It took Luis a moment to reply. 'Did you think,' he said at last, 'that my stepmother's taste in residences—and their contents—would be as ostentatious as her taste in clothes?'

'Yes, I did,' Katherine answered frankly. 'Am I wrong?'

He put down his pen and turned to her at last. 'Now how do I answer that? To anyone else, I'd give a positive yes or no. But to you, with your preference for the threadbare and the shabby things in life, I can only say—looking at it from your point of view—she opts for the expensive, the elegant——'

'In other words, for conspicuous consumption?'

'Yes. How did you know?' he drawled. 'A textbook description I couldn't improve on myself!'

'So why didn't you borrow the money from Aunt Olga?'

He saw her frown and commented, 'I wouldn't take money from my stepmother. It would have been like taking away what my father had bequeathed her.'

'Yet you took money from me.' She could not help the sharpness in her voice. It was put there by her worrying piece-by-piece discovery of the many unknown sides of the man at whom—she had to be frank—she had thrown herself.

'I'd take anything from you, Kate, anything and everything.'

His use of her pet name made her spine tingle. Her arm tightened round his. 'I've given you everything, darling,' she whispered, reaching up to kiss his cheek.

An air stewardess came round with trays of food. There was cold meat, pâté, bread, crackers and an apple pie. Luis bought two small bottles of wine. As he poured for her, he said:

'Does the food suit you? Or are you sorry now you didn't travel first class?' He was teasing, and she laughed.

'Against my principles,' she mumbled, chewing energetically. 'You should know that by now.'

'Don't I just!'

Katherine swallowed and there was a sinking feeling inside her as the plane hit turbulence. Staring up at him, she asked, 'What do you mean by that remark?'

His shoulders lifted and he continued eating. 'I've lived for a couple of weeks surrounded by your principles.' He shook his head at her solemnly. 'That's all I meant.'

For some reason unknown to her, her heart sank again, yet this time the plane was flying perfectly steadily.

Putting down her knife and fork, she said, her voice tight, 'I thought you enjoyed our honeymoon.'

He touched his mouth with a paper napkin. 'Surrounded by stacked, unwashed dishes?' He drained his glass and the trays were whisked away. He caught her chin and turned her face. 'I loved it, every minute, every second you spent in my arms.' His kiss was cool with the wine he had just drunk.

Her eyes were large as she stared up at him. 'Why are you talking like this? What's happened to you since we left home?' She searched his brown eyes. 'You're more serious, more——' She swallowed, hating the word. 'More businesslike.'

'Am I?' He traced her eyebrows. 'Maybe I'm thinking of the work ahead of me.'

'Work? What work?' There seemed to be a clutching hand at her throat.

'You lent me money, remember?' He gestured to the folder on the seat beside him. 'I've been working here beside you, trying to calculate the best way of using that money.'

'To save the business?'

'To help it to function better.'

'To improve the employees' future, so that they don't face dismissal?'

'Is that why you lent me the money, my Kate?'

'Partly.' His raised eyebrows questioned her further.

'But mostly because—well, I wanted you to have it. Only you.'

'Why?' Their eyes held. They were oblivious of everyone else, everything around them.

'Because you were the man of my dreams. That's why I added that condition.'

'Have I fulfilled your dreams?'

Katherine nodded. 'In every way. I hated all the other men my father had introduced to me. They all had money, like Dad. They were rich, yet they all wanted to make more, and still more.'

'You have money,' Luis challenged, removing his hand from her chin.

She fastened her arm on to his again. 'Only what Aunt Eleanor left me. I didn't get a paid job. I just lived on her bequest to me. Now I haven't any of it left.' Her smile showed her deep satisfaction. 'I've given it all to you.'

'Don't you mean to the business my father left me?'

'They're the same thing.'

He smiled and pulled open the folder, resuming his work. Katherine gazed out of the aircraft's window. She saw an endless expanse of sea, punctuated by an occasional ship. Holding on to the man beside her, whose character changes since they left home had bewildered her, she felt like a woman overboard floundering in the great emptiness beneath them without a rescue craft in sight.

Well, she thought with a small sigh, she had put herself into the water; she would just have to learn to swim. He moved against her and she found him gazing down into her face. There was the smile she had come to know so well—warm with admiration, fascinating, irresistible, ablaze with passion as he made caressing love to her, holding in check his own needs until he knew she was ready for the unleashing of his male desires.

'How many minutes is it since I told you how beautiful you are?' he asked softly.

'Hours, days,' she answered playfully, her spirits swinging like a speeded-up barometer reading from stormy to fine. This was more like the man she had lived with so joyously for the past two weeks. 'You can tell me now, if you like.' Her eyes looked impishly into his.

'You're beautiful,' he murmured against her ear. It was then that the pilot announced that very soon they would be approaching Madeira and preparing to land.

Luis moved away, pushing his papers back into the folder and packing them into a briefcase. To Katherine's sensitive eyes he had withdrawn into himself again. The few moments of verbal intimacy had gone as if they had never been.

The walk to the terminal building was silent. Soon they were through passport control and Luis was looking for their luggage. As he picked up their cases, handing one or two of the lighter bags to Katherine, a man emerged from a door leading outside.

At the sight of Luis, he beamed and extended his hand. The man was not very tall, dark-haired and, judging by his smile, overflowing with good humour. All the same, Katherine hung back, overcome by shyness.

'Good to see you back, Luis. Was your journey to London successful? You told me to speak English when we met. Now can I speak our own language?' Without awaiting an answer, the man proceeded to do so.

Luis answered him in Portuguese and half-turned, indicating Katherine. The man's eyes opened wide and swung to dwell with astonishment on the brown-haired, hazel-eyed girl who stood behind Luis de Freitas.

'*Wife? Your wife?' The man's amazement grew, then he frowned. 'You do not mean your——' The man hesitated, then used a word in Portuguese. The word seemed to make Luis angry.*

'*Kate, querida*, come, stand by me.' The impact of his return to the island he looked upon as his home had, Katherine noticed, even coloured his speech. Automatically she obeyed, only half aware of the noise and bustle around her.

Nearer now, she saw the lined face and sturdy physique of the man. He had plainly known the ups and downs of life, yet appeared to have weathered them all, emerging triumphant.

'Luis,' the man exclaimed, 'this lady is your bride? She

comes from the same country as your mother, and your
stepmother? And where you were born?'

'She does, Horacio,' Luis stated, his arm going possessively round Katherine's shoulders. 'She was my first and
only choice. Her name is Katherine. I would have no
other.'

Katherine's swift interrogating gaze saw the glimmer of
amusement in her husband's eyes as he looked down at
her. It passed swiftly.

'You married her when——?' the man called Horacio
enquired.

'Two weeks ago,' Katherine answered, then cleared her
throat which had become strangely dry. 'Our honeymoon
is over now.'

'Over, Katherine?' Horacio exclaimed. His glance indicated the world outside. 'Your honeymoon is just beginning. This island, the pearl of the Atlantic it has been
called—this is a honeymoon island, not your chilly
England. Here there is warmth and colour for almost all
the year. Of course,' a shrug of the shoulders dismissed
the words which had not yet been spoken, 'we have rain
in the so-called wintertime, but that comes in brief
showers, and is necessary to renew all life. No, no,' he
finished, 'your honeymoon is not over.' He turned, smiling
to Luis. 'Why should it ever be?'

'The taxi,' said Luis, 'you've brought it?'

'Of course, of course. Come, Senhora de Freitas,'
Horacio grinned up at Luis, 'your husband's uncle will
show you to the car. First, I will take two cases.' He
followed Katherine outside and called, 'Jorge, come, take
these. This is your new relative, a new and welcome
member of our family—Luis's bride. Katherine, this is
my son. He is being educated in Lisbon.'

Jorge, tall, thin with quiet eyes, had been standing
beside a taxi. He smiled shyly at Katherine. 'My cousin
Luis is good,' the young man said. 'You will be happy

with him. I am pleased you've come here.' He watched as his father stood some distance behind, talking to Luis. 'My father works hard. He has a taxi business.' The young man motioned to the waiting green and black taxi. 'In the university vacation, I help him by driving while he does his other work.'

A voice shouted and Jorge looked up. Horacio's hand pointed imperiously to the suitcases. 'Take them. There are more to come.' He added something in Portuguese which made Jorge frown, then look hard at Katherine. He shook his head as if he did not understand and obeyed his father.

'Jorge?' Katherine asked, as he helped her into the rear seat of the taxi. 'How is it that your father is Luis's uncle?'

Jorge spoke through the window. 'He is the brother of Luis's father, Pedro, who died.'

'And does your father look like Luis's father?'

'Perhaps Uncle Pedro was a little taller, and maybe not so good-humoured as my father.' He smiled. 'You know what I mean? Uncle Pedro was dedicated to his work, no matter what that work might be. He was——' Jorge scratched his head. 'How do you say it?'

'A slave to it?' Katherine suggested, tensed for the answer.

'That is it!' Jorge exclaimed. 'You have the words just right. If he had not worked so hard, maybe he might have lived longer, who knows?'

'So why—if he gave so much time to his business—did it fail, Jorge?' She asked the question so earnestly he stared at her.

'Fail?' He shook his head. 'I'm sorry. You will have to explain.'

'She will do no explaining, my son,' Horacio interrupted. 'She is Luis's bride and you will keep your eyes away from her.'

Jorge blushed deeply and Katherine felt sorry for him. Her husband, as he took his place beside her, was as irritated as his uncle.

'We were just talking, Mr—Senhor de Freitas,' she explained.

'No, no,' Horacio took his place at the wheel as his son settled into the front passenger seat, 'you must call me by my name, which is Horacio.'

'I'd prefer Uncle Horacio,' Katherine offered, and Horacio broke into laughter.

'Yes, yes, it sounds nice. Luis's new bride will call me Uncle Horacio.' They were driving along now. 'My brother Pedro would have liked you. But Luis tells me you have a will of your own.' He glanced in the driving mirror and pulled out to overtake. 'Yet you have been so quiet, I cannot see it.'

'Uncle,' Luis commented dryly, taking Katherine's hand, 'I am the one who sees it.' His eyes met Katherine's challengingly. 'And feels it,' he added.

'Feels it?' she retorted. 'I haven't hit you once.'

'You wouldn't dare,' Luis countered, smiling sardonically.

Horacio threw back his head in laughter again.

'No, this is where I feel it,' Luis went on. He took Katherine's hand, putting it to his heart. 'Here.'

'I didn't think you had such deep feelings,' she rejoined, smiling impudently.

'Ah, now I see what you mean about her,' Horacio said with a grin. 'She should make life very interesting for you, Luis. It is good to have a wife with spirit. Take note, Jorge, when you marry one day.'

Again Jorge coloured with embarrassment.

'You've remembered to make a booking at the hotel for me, Uncle?' Luis asked, gazing out of the car window.

'What are you——? Ah, yes, yes, of course. A suite, Luis. I have booked a suite for you.

Luis's head turned slowly, meeting his wife's startled gaze.

'I thought we were going to Aunt Olga's house,' said Katherine.

'You assumed that, my love,' he answered blandly. 'I did not confirm it.'

'But you didn't say we weren't!'

'Maybe,' Horacio intervened, 'he wanted to give you a surprise.'

'Oh, of course,' Katherine said doubtfully. She contrived to smile, 'Which hotel, Luis?'

'The Hotel Sereno,' Horacio answered. 'The best on the island. Is it not, Jorge?' He nudged his son, who seemed lost in thought. Jorge agreed, appearing hurriedly to gather his wits.

Katherine gazed at the scenery, seeing houses painted pink and a peach colour. Mountains dominated the view, towering high, their peaks lost in thin mist. Colour seemed to be everywhere, in the flowers and the plants, in the deep red of the sloping roofs and the intense blue of sea and sky.

'I suppose,' Katherine said thoughtfully, 'it is a good idea—a real honeymoon without having to cook or wash the dishes.' She questioned Luis, 'Does it have a swimming pool?'

'It has everything,' his uncle answered at once. 'Soft lights in the restaurant, suites with balconies, sitting-rooms, private bathrooms. Here,' he felt in his pocket as he drove, 'the leaflet advertising it, the tariff and so on.'

Before Katherine could reach across to take it, Luis had neatly intercepted her action, pushing the leaflet into his inner pocket. 'In a few minutes she will see for herself,' he said sharply.

Horacio flung back his head, as if enjoying some private joke. He nudged Jorge, who again looked a little startled, but managed a smile. 'You'll like it there,' he reassured

Katherine, adding his own praise almost as though his father had passed him a secret message.

'Darling,' her arm slipped through Luis's, 'I wanted to see your home. Luxury hotels are fine, but——'

'Don't tell me, I know they're against your principles,' Luis interrupted dryly. 'Any other woman,' he muttered between his teeth, 'would be chucking herself into my arms for arranging to take a suite at one of the best hotels. But you——' he freed his arm from her grip and looked as though he would like to strangle her, 'you have to make a fuss.'

Scarlet-cheeked, she maintained, 'I am *not* making a fuss! All I said was——'

'What is this,' Horacio demanded, signalling a right turn, 'against her principles?'

He swung the taxi in a semi-circle to park near the entrance to the hotel.

'It's a private conflict we're having, Horacio,' Luis declared, swinging his long legs to the ground and going round to help his wife.

Horacio stood beside Luis, indicating to his son to extract the cases from the taxi. A porter was approaching.

Katherine stared at her husband. 'Conflict? What conflict, Luis?' A note of uncertainty had crept into her voice, a strange kind of fear. 'At my house, there wasn't one. It was wonderful, the two of us sharing the work——'

'You are not there now. Nor am I.' The abrupt comment silenced her, but her apprehension grew from a spark to a lightning flash. She could feel in her bones that a storm was in the offing.

Horacio, serious now, asked, 'Luis? *Não compreendo.*'

Luis answered his uncle in Portuguese, which made Katherine enquire tartly, 'What have you just said?'

By Luis's silence, it seemed he was all set to ignore the question. His uncle filled the moment with a laughing, 'He's just confided to me how beautiful you are.'

Her frown was met by Luis's slow smile. In her annoyance at his evasiveness, she turned sharply away. The porter was a young man in uniform. '*Senhor*,' he said, then continued in his native Portuguese, touching his hand to his cap. When he had finished what appeared to be a welcoming speech, he nodded to Horacio, who nodded back, for the first time unsmiling. Then the boy spoke to Jorge, calling him Senhor de Freitas, too.

Watching the porter gather the cases, followed closely by Jorge, Katherine turned to Luis. 'How did he know the family name?'

'He's a good porter. Is he not, Horacio?'

Horacio's smile was back. 'The finest, Luis, like the Hotel Sereno.'

'You've been here before?' Katherine asked.

'Many times.'

'Wining and dining,' Horacio offered.

'With my stepmother,' Luis added with a quirk of his eyebrow. 'She's suspicious of me already, Horacio.'

His uncle let out another of his deep laughs. 'Ah, those "other women" these young brides hate so much.'

Luis's hand gripped Katherine's elbow. 'You will attend to reception?' Luis asked his uncle.

'Yes, yes, I'll deal with everything.'

They passed through glass swing doors. There seemed to be glass everywhere and the overall effect was one of light—daylight, sunlight, reflected golden light from the sparkling blue of the outside pool which was clearly visible down curving stairs.

'This way,' Luis urged, 'the lift is coming.' The young porter had his hand on the call button.

'Surely you must register first?' Katherine queried.

Luis did not answer, sweeping her into the lift. The bellboy waited, his hand ready to operate the button for the required floor. Luis told him and the lift whisked swiftly and almost silently upwards.

Katherine stared up at her husband, but he was watching the floor indicator.

'How did you know the suite number?' she challenged.

His smile was lazy. 'I'm psychic. Did I forget to tell you?'

'I suppose your uncle told you. Using your own language.'

'One of my languages. English is my first, since I was born in Britain.'

The suite was a short walk from the lift. The porter was waiting outside with the luggage grouped around him. He smiled broadly as Luis appeared, producing two keys and using one. He stood back, handed the keys to Luis and bowed them in. Then he proceeded to move the cases into the living area.

When Luis nodded, handing him a tip, the young porter looked at it and went red. '*Obrigado, muito obrigado,*' he said, backing out.

'That must have been quite a tip,' Katherine commented, frowning. 'You gave it to him as casually as all the rich men my father contrived to marry me to.'

He smiled to himself, removing his jacket. 'My own father was not exactly poor.'

'Meaning that, when he was alive, you picked up his habits?'

He gave her a narrow look which made her quiver inside. He loosened his tie while walking slowly towards her. 'I don't like your sarcasm, *amada*. It grates on me.' His hands gripped her arms, jerking her against him. 'This is what I do to bitchy women—especially when the woman concerned is my wife.'

His lips prised open her mouth, his hand lifted to cup the back of her head. She was virtually a prisoner of his leashed desire. The kiss bore into the very essence of her. It tasted and savoured all the sweetness it found, pounding at the door of the resistance which had strangely built up in her almost from the moment of their arrival.

A moaning sound told herself as well as the man whose ravishment of her mouth was putting a frightening weakness into her legs, that her deepest instincts were being stirred. A few moments more, she knew, as he must have known, and he could do what he liked with her. The knock on the outer door angered him and he shouted over his shoulder, '*Ir-se embora!*' Retreating footsteps obeyed the terse command.

Katherine's eyes flew open. 'You've told them to go, just like that? But we're guests. You shouldn't talk to the hotel staff like that!'

His hold became more bruising as he released her head and fastened again on her arms.

'Supporting the underdog, Kate? Always on the side of the downtrodden?' he sneered.

'You've changed,' she whispered, gripping his shirt collar from which the tie had been discarded. 'Where's the man I married, the man I lived with so happily back home?' For a long moment she searched his face, and noticed for the first time a hard shape to his jaw, an even harder look in his eyes.

At last she realised how his hold on her had tightened. 'Please, Luis, you're hurting!' There were a few moments more of agony, then he threw her from him.

'You must be wanting to wash or shower, change your clothes. The bathroom is through there. When you've finished, I shall follow.'

His tone had gone flat.

There was a sunken bath in a white-tiled bathroom. When Katherine stepped down into the bursting bubbles of foam she sighed into the deep relaxation which the whole luxurious ambience and the satin-soft water invited. Even her father's house had not offered such expensive self-indulgence as this. Yet she had rebelled against his chosen way of like. Should she not be rebelling at this?

It was easy to push away mutinous thoughts in such a situation. Later, she promised herself, I'll go back to my Cinderella role, when Luis takes me to his home. Except that his home—hadn't he said so?—was nothing like the simple surroundings she had left behind.

As she towelled herself, pulling round her a robe which she found hanging on the door, she heard Luis's voice speaking in Portuguese. At first she wondered if it was the person who had tried earlier to gain admittance. Then she realised that he was using the telephone. Emerging from the bathroom, she heard him say his uncle's name as if arguing with him. He glanced at her, spoke again and rang off.

Under his appraising eyes, she coloured. He seemed to be mocking her silently, something the Luis she had known back home would never have done. He had been a friend as well as lover. Here, in this hotel, he had undergone a frightening change. Even now, in the intimacy of the surroundings, he was distant, aloof, a handsome but tormenting stranger.

'I can't understand why——' she ventured, fidgeting under his gaze. A raised eyebrow invited her to continue. 'Why returning to the country you live in should have such a—a disastrous effect on your personality.'

He was unfastening his shirt buttons, stripping off the garment and throwing it down. Her eyes traced the leanness of him, looked at his chest, the strong arms which had held her so many times in the days since their marriage. No, that hadn't changed, except that although a barrier seemed to have grown between them, his magnetism had, conversely, grown stronger.

That barrier had to be demolished. She couldn't stand this inexplicable sense of alienation from him which had descended, threatening to destroy the happiness they had known and which, she had—perhaps naïvely?—thought would last a lifetime.

Arms wide, she ran to him, clasping his waist, resting her head against the dark spread of hair across his chest. Her arms tried vainly to shake him. 'Tell me you still love me,' she pleaded, 'because I still love you. I can't help it, Luis.' She gazed upwards, her glance moving over the firm chin, the sensual lips, the strong nose, meeting at last two brown, enigmatic eyes.

As she gazed, so those eyes flared and she knew his passion had been ignited. His mouth came down to taste the shoulder his hands had bared, to skim her skin, making it tingle.

The bathrobe was unfastened, lips trailed a fiery path down to the softly rounded breasts he cupped in his hand. Her breathing quickened as he teased and caressed. 'Every part of you is mine,' he said huskily, 'all your beauty, your warmth, your loveliness. I want you, Kate,' he drew away reluctantly, 'and if it weren't for the world around us going about its business and intruding into ours, I'd take you, here and now.' Another tap on the door elicited a curse from him.

He indicated that she should close the wrap and went to the door. There was a brief conversation in Portuguese. The man in the corridor seemed to Katherine to be disproportionately deferential. She guessed it was because they had become known, through Luis's uncle, Horacio, who seemed to have booked the suite, as newlyweds.

'We're dining here,' Luis announced as he closed the outer door, then the inner door on to the tiny lobby. 'We won't be disturbed.' As she frowned, he asked, 'Would you rather have dined in the restaurant or the grillroom?'

Katherine's shoulders lifted. 'I was just thinking that, before we came here, you would have asked me first and we would have made the decision together.' Her smile broke through. 'All the same I agree.' She reached up to run a finger over his top lip. 'I should like to be alone with you. It's seemed a long time.'

He consulted his watch. 'A few hours, that's all, you minx.'

Her smile held, but she persisted, 'I really meant—the "you" I married, the "you" who skimped and scraped with me in that old house where I lived, where *we* lived for nearly two weeks.'

His smile in return held a touch of hardness, but it quickly melted away. 'That "me" you married, *amada*, is still here inside me.'

'But it's hidden beneath the arrogant side of you which has come out on top since you arrived back here?' Her tone was guileless, but her gaze taunted.

His eyes revealed ignited desire again and he reached round to give her a sharp slap. 'You deserve to be ravished here and now, Senhora de Freitas. In fact——'

The telephone drew his brows into a frown. His arms dropped from her waist and he answered the call abruptly. Again he spoke in Portuguese. '*Sim. Obrigado.*' He turned to Katherine. 'Fifteen minutes, then they will serve dinner here. Can you be ready?'

Smiling she nodded, edging her way towards the suit-cases, 'I have to find a dress.'

'Why bother?' he drawled. 'Your ravishment hasn't been cancelled, *querida*, merely postponed.'

A hand flew to her mouth. 'I haven't unpacked. Is there time—?'

'Leave it,' he dismissed. 'It will be done for you later.'

'Is that what the first knock on the door was about and you told them to go away?'

'It was. Do I get another lecture on how to speak to the hotel staff?' He spoke with a smile which softened the edginess of his tone.

'Not now,' she flipped back, 'but when I've got more time ...' She dodged his playful fist.

While Katherine spread her evening gown on the bed, Luis disappeared into a small room leading off the main bedroom. Katherine had not had time to look in there, but she assumed it was a dressing-room.

The deep lavender-coloured dress slipped silkily over her head to rest across her shoulders. It narrowed from rope-thin shoulder straps to a deep point, tantalising in the cleft it revealed. From the waist it smoothed over her slender hips to her ankles, while her silver-sandalled feet peeped from beneath the hem.

Turning from the mirror, she stopped every movement. Luis leaned negligently against the dressing-room doorway, hands in pockets, his dark evening suit intensifying the attractiveness of his proud bearing. Brown eyes narrowed as they rested on the slim figure of his wife. The wordless appraisal sent shivers down her spine.

A frown pleated her brow. There were words in the air, but they were floating about like feathers and she could not catch them. Something should be said to break the tense silence. 'Luis?' she whispered, listening for his answer.

He spoke, not only with words, but also with action, pulling from his pocket a long, narrow box. 'For my bride who spurns riches,' he said, 'from her husband whose extravagance on such an occasion she will, I hope, forgive.'

Bewildered, her hand, if not her mind, accepted the gift. Her hand shook faintly as her fingers lifted the lid. It was a necklace of diamonds!

CHAPTER FIVE

AGHAST, she looked up at him. She could not, would not, accept it.

'Luis,' she whispered, 'you, of all men....' His expression was deeply serious. She moistened her lips. 'You should know——' I can't say yes, she thought, yet I can't refuse. The look on his face dared her. It was a challenge she knew she would have to accept. Then it came to her.

'The money,' she said, 'you couldn't have afforded to buy this. Back home I paid—I paid for everything, everywhere we went. So—so you must have borrowed the money. Your uncle, Horacio? His savings, perhaps?'

'Perhaps. You like it?'

'It's absolutely beautiful, Luis!'

'Then if I made sacrifices, they were worth it. If you like it, that's all that matters.' A fist brushed lightly beneath her chin. 'Don't frown. The recipient should never question the giver's means of giving. Here, let me put it on for you.'

Obediently she turned, and when his fingers brushed the back of her neck the nerves of her skin tingled exquisitely. Hands held her shoulders and turned her to the mirror. The sparkle of the gemstones reflected back into her eyes as they gazed and lifted to meet his reflection.

'They're beautiful, Luis, just beautiful,' she whispered, lifting her hands to cover his. 'And I love them all the more because you had to make sacrifices to buy them.' Slowly she turned round. Her hands slid up his jacket to his shoulders. With a small tug she urged him down, then, standing on tiptoe, she kissed him.

His arms came round her and she was crushed against

him. His lips caught her exhalation of breath, trapping the air in her lungs. His hands stroked her bare shoulders, her upper arms, gripping them as if holding them more securely round his neck. When he lifted his head, he murmured endearments, but they were in Portuguese.

Her fingers felt for his cheeks, stroking them feverishly. 'Luis darling—oh, darling,' her words came through the taut muscles of her throat, 'I love you, I love you!' With her breasts pressed against him, she gazed into his face. 'How many times shall I tell you?'

'Before I believe you?' His lips touched the corners of her mouth. 'I believe you now, but carry on telling me, *amada*, for the rest of your life.'

'When will you tell me back?' The anxious note could not be mistaken.

'You want me to put into words what you must know I feel every time I make love to you? These hands of mine,' he held them away, looking at them, leaving her clinging, 'they won't leave you alone, don't you know that?' His arms were round her again. 'I have to exercise the greatest control, no matter where we are, to stop them reaching out and touching you, holding you to me.' A finger ran lightly down her nose. 'In case you run away.'

Outside the door, there was the faint rattle of a laden trolley. 'Our dinner,' she exclaimed, pulling free. 'I wouldn't run away at this moment, that's for sure! I'm so hungry!'

Luis watched with amusement as Katherine did more than justice to the food the hotel had provided. She drank the last drops of her wine while Luis rang for the coffee.

'I wish,' she said, 'I could thank the chef. That was wonderful.'

'Do you want to thank the chef?' Luis picked up the telephone, holding it out.

Katherine's eyes opened wide. 'I can't do that. He's sure to be Portuguese. He wouldn't understand a word.'

Luis still offered her the phone. 'Try it. Just say who you are, then give him your thanks.'

Uncertainty made her hands reach out slowly. Luis's smile mocked her lack of confidence, and this spurred her on. Then she smiled back. 'I can't. I don't know his number.'

Luis strolled round and while Katherine held the telephone, he dialled. 'Now listen.'

There came a stream of Portuguese in her ear. Her eyes widened still more, but she moistened her lips, saying, 'Thi-this is Mrs—I mean Senhora—de Freitas.' There was a profound silence. 'The—meal we—my husband and I—have just eaten—it was wonderful. Thank you.'

She listened for a burst of abuse in an alien tongue. Instead, the voice said, in accented English, 'Senhora de Freitas, I am delighted. You pay me a great big compliment. I have cooked it especial good for you, just for you. And your husband. Thank you, *senhora*, thank you.'

'No, thank *you*, Mr—I mean, Chef. I just had to tell you.'

The telephone was taken from her and put aside. 'You see,' Luis commented, 'how easy it was.'

'He spoke English!'

'He trained in a number of countries, including English-speaking ones.'

Katherine frowned. 'How do you know all this?'

'I told you, I've stayed here before.' He was, she sensed, in danger of reverting to that remoteness which never seemed far away.

She made to go towards him, but again a knock intervened. Luis laughed at her motion of gnashing her teeth and invited the room maid to enter. The table was cleared. The coffee was on a silver salver, complete with silver coffee pot and cream jug. It was placed on a low glass-topped table near a couch. The maid left, smiling happily.

There was a long, warm silence as they drank. 'Do you know something, darling?' Katherine remarked, putting down her empty cup. 'I'm looking forward to living on this island of yours. I've only been here a few hours, but already it seems to have got into my bloodstream.'

'Good, *querida*,' he reached out and drew her across his lap, 'because you are in *my* bloodstream. Your chemistry and mine,' slowly his fingers moved down the shoulder straps of her dress, 'are so compatible they keep crying out to merge and mix.'

His dark eyes searched hers and twin flames were lit. 'They're combustible, too. I've only got to look at you to feel an explosion is imminent.' His lips feathered her throat, reaching the cleft. It seemed he could not tolerate the way the dress hid her shape. With impatient hands he pushed the dress down, revealing the silky whiteness of her breasts.

Katherine gasped as the possessive touch of his lips aroused her unbearable desire. Her hands linked round his neck and his mouth moved to claim hers. As she pressed against him, the roughness of his jacket gave rise to exquisite feelings of vulnerability inside her. The hardness of the diamond necklace he had given her pressing into her skin reminded her, insidiously, of worldly things.

Diamond necklace.... Even as she responded to his kisses, her mind wondered hazily how he had found the money—and it must have been a considerable amount—to pay for such a thing.

Luis lifted his head, looking at her with some irritability. 'What's wrong?'

She could not tell him of her doubts. 'Just—just——' She had to think of a plausible excuse. Her smile was winsome. 'I'd like to—to go somewhere. See the bright lights. Go dancing?' It was the last thing she wanted to do, but he seemed to believe her, and surprisingly, to understand her request.

'I must wait, is that what you're saying? An hour or so, since waiting sharpens the appetite? You're an impudent little witch. I can only make love to my wife when *she* decides!' He whispered in her ear, 'I shall punish you for this, my darling. In the night, when we make love, you'll be sorry you kept me waiting.'

He put her aside and leaned across to pull her shoulder straps into position. 'There's dancing in one of the rooms. Tidy yourself and we'll look for the "life" and the bright lights.'

They found it by descending a staircase and seeing through the outer walls of glass the lights of Funchal twinkling against the velvet blackness of the evening. Hand in hand they walked, and Katherine's hand gripped Luis's in a little-girl excitement. A jolt of conscience hit her when she thought about the luxurious surroundings in which she found herself, but she knew it would not last.

Surely, for a few days, her conscience would let her enjoy this present, this gift of an extended honeymoon Luis was giving her. It still troubled her how he had found the means to pay for their stay in such an obviously expensive hotel, but she pushed the niggling anxiety to the back of her mind.

It was a restaurant they entered through doors which were being held open for them. Luis acknowledged with a brief nod the two men's greetings, and Katherine heard them mention his name.

Her hand was through his arm and she tugged on it, gaining his attention. 'That personal touch, it's very pleasant,' she told him. He smiled down at her, then spoke in Portuguese to a man who appeared to be the head waiter. Luis gestured towards the darkest corner, although the whole room was illuminated sparingly with recessed lighting.

The man bowed and showed them to a table partly hidden in an alcove. Luis ordered drinks and the man, looking from Luis to Katherine said,

'Senhora de Freitas, I have offered my good wishes for

your future happiness to Senhor de Freitas. Now may I offer them to you.' He bowed again and went away.

Katherine's warm cheeks glowed in the light from the flickering candle on their table. 'The Madeiran people are so friendly,' she exclaimed. 'This is a wonderful hotel. Thank you for bringing me here, darling.' Her hand reached out to touch his as it rested on the table.

He moved his hand to hold hers. 'So a short stay in such a luxury-laden atmosphere doesn't offend your social conscience?'

' "Short" is the important word,' she retorted, smiling. 'I'm just about able to pacify my principles by telling them it's not for long.'

'Suppose I were to tell you our stay here could be indefinite?'

His face was in shadow, which meant she could not see the teasing smile she was sure was there. 'Even if you said it, I'd know it wasn't true. No man who married a girl for the money she could give him, as you did, would be able to afford to pay for more than a few days here. In fact, you might be using some of that money I gave you to finance this holiday. Am I right?'

Luis leaned forward and pressed the tip of her nose. 'No, you're wrong.'

She caught his hand and held it with both of hers. 'So it's Uncle Horacio's money, after all.'

The wine waiter approached and served the drinks. Luis spoke to him in his own language and the man looked at Katherine, nodding happily and addressing her in Portuguese.

Luis explained, 'He offers his congratulations and hopes we will be very happy.'

Katherine ventured, '*Obrigado.*' The man beamed and went on his way.

'Full marks for diplomacy,' Luis commented, a mocking note in his voice. 'As the daughter of a rich businessman, I suppose, it was instilled into you, whether you liked it or not, at an early age.'

Katherine laughed. 'I love hearing you being sarcastic on that subject. I know you were trying to annoy me. Instead, you've made me very pleased.'

Luis leaned forward into the light and Katherine caught his questioning frown. 'You were ridiculing rich businessmen and I love you for it.' She lifted his hand to her lips.

The soft music grew louder, inviting the patrons to dance. Katherine turned in her seat and watched the first couples moving together. 'Luis.' He leant towards her to listen. 'It's been a long time since I've danced.'

He smiled, then shook his head with mock reproof. 'Stupid of you to cut yourself off so completely from social contact. But,' he gestured towards the softly illuminated dance floor, 'you wouldn't want to mix with the rich and the privileged, would you?'

His deliberate provocation annoyed her. 'I told you, it's only for a short time, so——?' Her large eyes held his in an unspoken plea, but he still did not move. 'Please, Luis,' she spoke each word clearly, 'will you dance with me?'

'You're becoming an expert on reversing the traditional roles. First you propose to me, now you're importuning me. The Women's Lib movement would be proud of you.'

'Will you stop being so—so superior! All right,' she half rose, 'if you won't dance with me, some other man will!'

He was round the table and jerking her to her feet before she had finished the sentence. On the dance floor, in the half-darkness, he held her as closely as movement would allow. The music was romantic, the tempo slow. Their bodies made intimate contact, his hands on her hips, her arms crossing behind his neck.

Their cheeks pressed together, his head inclining a little to reach hers. Briefly, their thighs touched and touched again. He whispered, 'I told you your face was heart-shaped.'

Katherine nodded, too happy to speak.

'I asked you if that was the only heart you had. My love, I know differently now.' In the semi-darkness his hand moved, first to span her ribs, then cupping a breast. 'Now I know your real heart beats here. When we make love, it throbs under my hand.'

'For you, Luis, only for you.' Her head went back so that she could gaze into his shadowed face. He held her hips again. 'Never for any other man, that I promise you.'

His lips found her neck and she shivered at the touch of them.

'It's time, sweetheart, we returned to our suite.' He smiled into her eyes. 'We won't be disturbed, I can promise you that.'

Taking her hand, he led her to the lifts. The hotel staff, discreetly looked the other way. Returning to their suite, Katherine discovered that the suitcases had been emptied, their clothes put away. The cupboards were filled with them, the drawers neatly packed.

Seeing her surprise, Luis said, 'I told you the room maid would do it for you.'

'Luis,' she exclaimed, 'it's wonderful! It's almost as if we were royalty.'

He came to her, pulled her close. 'We're newlyweds, and all the world loves those.'

She shook her head vigorously. 'I still can't get over the efficiency of this place—the chef, the hotel staff. How many stars did you say it had?'

He returned her smile. The lift of his shoulders came straight from his Portuguese inheritance. 'A hundred. As many stars as are in the sky. Who cares? It's good, eh? You like the Hotel Sereno?'

Her arms reached up, locking round his neck. '*Sim,*

querido, I like it very much.' He laughed at the accent she had assumed.

'Do you know what?' He was speaking perfect English again. 'I *like* my wife. I *like* her so much, I want——' His mouth cut off the sentence. When the kiss stopped, he finished, 'I want her. Then I shall want her again. And again.' His mouth lowered once more and tasted hers. 'Have your shower, and whatever else it is you do. Make yourself ready for me, *amada*.'

Katherine reached up to kiss him. 'You're arrogant and a male chauvinist, but I love you.'

With Luis's help, she unfastened the necklace, putting it with reverent care into its box. She revered it, not for its monetary value, which was considerable, but because it was a gift from her husband.

He watched as she put it into a drawer, nodding when she asked, 'Is that all right?'

When Katherine emerged from the steamy, perfumed atmosphere of the bathroom, she heard Luis's voice. It came drifting through the partition which had been unfolded to divide the living from the sleeping area. He seemed once again to be talking on the telephone.

Slipping a softly-clinging peach-coloured nightgown over her head, Katherine reasoned that, now he had more money—the money she had given him—his main concern would be to make every effort to get his business on its feet again.

Over her nightdress she pulled a matching negligee, then ran a comb through her softly-styled hair. Luis appeared behind her, having entered through a communicating door. With an inexplicable shyness, her eyes lifted to meet his. She saw admiration and desire in the half-closed eyes.

'My wife is beautiful,' he said softly. 'A man couldn't have been offered a better woman to live with and mate with——'

She turned and ran her nails down the mat of hair revealed by the opened neck of his shirt. He laughed, putting his hands over hers, stilling their movement. 'It was my money you were after,' she accused, her eyes alight with laughter.

He dropped into a low chair, pulling her on to his knees. 'There was something else, too, my clawing little cat. Money alone wouldn't have tempted me. Something precious, which few women possess these days.' His mouth was tormenting her throat, making her head hang back with joyful abandon. 'Innocence,' he said between kisses, 'and the promise of unrestrained passion beyond that innocence.'

He lifted her head, carried her to the bed and put her down. 'Ten minutes and I'll be back,' he promised. He closed the bathroom door and turned the taps full on.

Katherine scrambled off the bed and made for the comb on the dressing-table. Passing the chair on which Luis had hung his jacket, she brushed against it, and dislodged a piece of paper from the pocket. It fell to the carpet and she recognised it as the leaflet advertising the hotel which Horacio had handed to her in the taxi. Luis had intercepted it and put it away. 'She'll see the place for herself soon,' he'd said.

Having seen the hotel, however, she wanted even more to read about it, enjoy the photographs and explanations of its amenities. 'Hotel Sereno,' the leaflet announced in large letters above a photograph. 'One of Madeira's top hotels. Relax when you wish, or dance the night away. You can choose.' There was the date of its opening, not so many years ago. There was the name of proprietor ... Senhor Luis Pedro de Freitas, it announced, was the owner of the Hotel Sereno.

Unbelievingly, her legs weak with the knowledge that would change the course of her life, Katherine sank to the bed. It couldn't—it mustn't be true!

CHAPTER SIX

THE bathroom door opened and Luis emerged, a towelling robe tied loosely round him. 'Sweetheart,' he said, holding out a hand, 'come——' Then he saw her face.

'No,' Katherine hurled at him, standing up 'I will *not* come, not now or ever again!' Her breath came quickly, all colour had gone from her cheeks, her eyes blazed into his. 'This——' she held up the leaflet, 'this is why. So who's the owner of this place, this—this palace built to accommodate millionaires? Senhor Luis de Freitas. You—you!'

His head was high, his expression taking on the remoteness she had come to fear.

'What does that make you?' she challenged, tension stiffening her body. 'A millionaire, too?'

'And if I am?'

'I'd hate you, with a terrible hatred.'

'Then you'd better hate me, *querida*.'

She had hoped—she had not really believed.... But he was! 'So I was tricked—by my father, by Aunt Olga—but most of all by you!'

'Who made that "condition" of marriage?' he asked coolly, 'you or I?'

'Only because I honestly believed the story you told me about your failing business.' She looked about her. 'Some *failing business* you had! And I made you a loan to help you, to make sure your employees didn't go hungry.' She turned away, to hide her trembling lips, her filling eyes. 'How you must have laughed, you and my father!' She swung round, anger drying her tears. 'I'm going to call him on the phone. I'm going to tell my precious father just what I think of him. No wonder my mother left him!'

Her hand reached for the telephone, gripping it, but it was prised from her fingers by his. He replaced the receiver and stood shielding it. 'What's wrong?' she taunted. 'Can't you *afford* an overseas call?'

'Your father is ill, remember? You're not adding to his troubles by pouring out your fury on to him.'

'What are you doing, protecting your fellow conspirator?' she accused.

'No,' his smile was twisted, 'just keeping the quarrel in the family.'

Family! Of course, she was his "family" now. 'It won't stay that way,' she burst out. 'As from this moment, I have no family. I'll go back to the life I left behind, the life I never really wanted to leave.'

Luis advanced on her, but his hands stayed in his robe pockets. 'Are you trying to lay the blame at my door?'

She backed away, but he followed. Her heart was pounding and she was afraid.

'Who made that "condition"?' he persisted. 'Who *asked* me to marry her? You, no one else. I didn't need your money, but since it went with you, I took it. I went along with your "condition" for my own purpose. I wanted a woman in my life—a woman to marry, not just to sleep with.'

'You acted a lie, and I hate you for it!'

'So you hate me. I'm cut to the heart. But you're mine, my dear Kate, *mine*. No other man's, ever. Do you understand that?'

'I'm not living with a man I can't stand the sight of!' The words were coming of their own accord, she couldn't stop them, nor did she really want to.

'You're living with me for the rest of your life, even if I have to lock you in from morning till night.'

Her eyes sought his, aghast. 'I really believe you would! Well, I've got news for you. I'm going back to where I came from. I'm getting a divorce!'

'That, my darling wife, is the last thing you'll do.' Luis's hands fastened on to her arms and he looked so murderous, she was almost convinced he meant what he said. He dragged her across the room towards the bed, but she cried,

'I refuse to sleep with you!' She struggled, pulling away from him. 'I'll ring for help, I'll ring reception——' Then it struck her what a prisoner she really was. He had only to give an order—or cancel it—and he would be obeyed. Every single member of staff was under his control. And so was she.

All the same, she twisted and turned as he started to remove her negligee, but it was there on the floor. Her nightgown joined it. Wrapping her arms about her, she made for the bathroom, but he caught her and swung her in his arms and on to the bed.

Now his towelling robe had gone and she felt the roughness of him as he lay beside her. His mouth, as it roamed her body, did not spare her, no matter where it touched. The very harshness of his lovemaking aroused responses she had never experienced before.

When his mouth claimed and tantalised the soft skin of her breasts, teasing until she felt her body arching against him in abandoned delight, she was forced to admit, through the mist in which her thoughts were groping, that his power over her was complete and that she, in her turn, would never again be complete without him.

Afterwards, it was not the same as the other times, when making love had had them reaching for each other. In her old and well-worn bed, Katherine had lain cradled in his arms, while hers had held him as though he was a rock in a wild sea and she would drown without him.

This time Luis turned from her, leaving her to cover them both. She lay there surfeited but joyless, loved by her lover, yet unloved. She lifted a hand to still her trembling lips. She would not give him the satisfaction of knowing of her distress.

At last she turned on her side, hoping sleep would come, but it evaded her and she edged to her other side, facing his back. Again she tried, but it was no use.

Her hand reached out spontaneously, lightly touching his hip. 'Luis?' It had been a whisper, maybe he hadn't heard. 'Luis?' Was he asleep?

He jerked on to his back. 'What's wrong?' She had never heard his voice so grating. 'Haven't I given you satisfaction? Do you want more?'

She cringed from his touch on her thigh. In the light from the moon, she saw the flick of his anger. She swore his lips drew back in a snarl at her involuntary reaction.

'I'm sorry,' was his cutting reply, 'I have no more to give.'

When Katherine awoke the day was bright, the morning sun flooding the room.

Her hand went automatically across the bed to make contact with the man she loved, but there was nothing there. Then it all came back and she rolled moaning on to her face. 'Loved?' she thought bitterly. Hated was the word she should have used. Yet, she thought, still drowsy, how can a woman hate the man she loves?

'Your breakfast is waiting for you.' Luis's voice came from the small room leading off the main bedroom. He was tying his tie. He wore a business suit. The laughing, relaxed man in open-necked shirt and slacks might never have existed.

'Where are you going?' she asked, frowning.

'To work, where else? The truth is out—as if it wasn't staring you in the face all the time.'

Katherine sat up, then realised that her only covering was the quilt. This she held to her under Luis's sarcastic gaze. 'Would you explain that?' she asked.

With a long sigh, he consulted his wristwatch. 'Your

reason must surely have told you that my stepmother could have lent me any money I needed.'

'No, my reason didn't. I assumed you were—well, too proud to ask her. Anyway, if your father's business really had failed, he wouldn't have had much to leave, would he? "Well provided for" could have meant the house here which she lets you share.'

'Another piece of false reasoning,' he replied. 'The house is mine, not hers.'

'How was I to know,' she blazed back, 'that you were all telling so many lies? The moment I saw you I noticed that—that arrogance of yours. I knew a man without money shouldn't have had the confidence you had, but I assumed it was a kind of spill-over from your more affluent past, plus an inheritance from the non-English side of you. I should have trusted my instinct.'

He walked slowly towards her. 'You certainly should. Then we would not have made a loveless marriage.'

His words were like pistol shots riddling her body. She wanted to scream with pain. She loved him more than she loved any other human being, yet she could never again tell him so. Her head touched her covered, bent knees. One day, she thought miserably, I'll leave him, just like my mother left my father.

Her head came up. 'Look at you,' she hit out, 'all dressed up—the big business tycoon in person! Yes, you've got a lot in common with my father, and I don't just mean tricking unsuspecting, trusting females!'

Luis tore away her covering and his hands fastened round her neck. Her hands fastened over his wrists, tearing at them. His hold loosened slightly as he caught the unconscious appeal in her eyes. 'One day,' he muttered through his rigid mouth, 'I'll——'

'It's our honeymoon, Luis,' she said brokenly. 'Even if you did marry me under false pretences, it's still our honeymoon.'

'The honeymoon,' he said curtly, 'is over.' He went from the room.

For a long time Katherine lay staring at the closed door. Her imagination tricked her into seeing him coming back, taking her into his arms—and loving her with the passionate tenderness of those unforgettable days which they spent in her shabby, but real-life, bedroom.

Her eyes roamed, taking in the expensive elegance. This, she thought, was not 'real life'. It was all pretence and pretentiousness. Wonderful for a holiday, a prolonged vacation—or for truly loving newlyweds. But to be married to the *owner*—something some women would glory in, but which she rejected with her whole heart.... She pulled the cover over her head, then lowered it, remembering the breakfast which awaited her.

It consisted of rolls, toast, honey and marmalade. A coffee pot stood, warmed by a heater. She would ring for the room maid and tell her to take it away. Her hand was reaching for the telephone when she checked it. Waste all that food? No, she couldn't do that! Wouldn't she in truth be acting the part of the owner's wife, frivolously sending to the waste bin valuable, nourishing foodstuffs, completely thoughtless of those in need?

Anyway—she drew on Luis's bathrobe, which lay where he had thrown it—she was hungry. It did not take long for the breakfast to disappear inside her. Tiptoeing to the double windows which, when open, led on to a balcony, she studied the view of Funchal spread beneath her, seeing with awe the sweep of the mountains and the bay.

There was within her, despite the events of the night, an unquenchable excitement. If only, she thought, Luis would take her sightseeing, show her the summits and the valleys, how the people lived. If only.... How many times must her mother had wished her husband, Halmar, could be at her side, instead of working himself to exhaustion point every day of their married life?

Slowly Katherine was beginning to understand her mother's point of view. Yet wasn't this just what she had tried to avoid as her own fate? And hadn't fate played a cruel trick? Turning from the window, she resolved that, husband or no husband, she would go out and see for herself, unaccompanied, if necessary—then she had an idea.

It so pleased her that she dressed quickly, in slacks and blouse, clothes such as she had worn at home. Luis had married her knowing her true nature. Not for anyone could she alter it, despite her changed position on the social scale. It wasn't in her to play the elegant, faintly superior wife of a millionaire. She would find the real people of this island and mix with them.... What's more, she thought defiantly, I know the way to make contact.

The lift came at a touch. To her relief, it was empty and it took her with speed to the ground floor. Leaving the duplicate key to the suite at reception, she swung away, only to be called by the man at the desk.

'Senhora de Freitas?' She turned. 'You are going out?' A young woman beside him was using the counter telephone. 'I should be very pleased,' the man said, 'if you would be good enough to inform me where you are going?'

His politeness could not be faulted, but Katherine frowned. On whose orders was he questioning her? The man's expression had changed to that of subordinate in the presence of a disdainful, overbearing guest. Katherine could not bear it.

'Of course I'll tell you,' she told him with disarming openness. Her unconsciously sweet smile brought a discreet, but admiring smile in answer. Relief was there too, Katherine noted, reminding herself never again to give any member of the hotel staff cause to be self-effacing with her. 'I'm——'

'You're what?' From the suite of offices at the rear of the reception area, Luis emerged, hands in pockets, head high, expression unreadable.

The man in reception followed the counter round the corner. The girl put down the telephone and followed him. Luis called to her 'Thanks, Maria,' and she smiled her gratitude and admiration.

'So you've told the staff to check on me!' Katherine's face was flushed with anger. 'One delays me by asking where I'm going, the other calls you by phone. Well, if you want to know where I'm going, you'll either have to come with me, or set a private detective on my trail!' With which statement, spoken quietly but with vehemence, she swung round and made for the glass swing doors.

Her footsteps rang out and she wished the reception area were not so large. The door-keeper turned as she approached, lifted his hand as if in acknowledgment and opened the door for her. Katherine gave a swift look over her shoulder and found that her husband was still there. So it was he who had signalled to the man. What had that signal meant? In a few seconds she knew the answer.

A taxi bearing the words 'Hotel Sereno' drew up outside. The door-keeper escorted her to it and spoke a few words in Portuguese to the driver. He nodded, looked with respect mingled with appreciation at his passenger and asked her, in commendable English, where she would like to be taken.

'Please,' she said, 'will you drive a short distance from the hotel? Then I'll tell you.' The man nodded, saluted the door-keeper and drove towards the entrance, pulling up and letting the engine idle. 'Do you—do you know Mr—Senhor Horacio de Freitas?' Katherine asked.

'*Sim, sehora*, I know Senhor Horacio well. You wish to go to his office?'

'Office? You mean Senhor Horacio is a—is a business-man?'

The taxi driver laughed. 'He runs a business, *senhora*, but I do not think he would call himself that. He is not like Senhor Luis de Freitas, not at all. Nor is he like his brother Pedro, who was Senhor Luis's father. Except perhaps in size——' he held his hand in front of his middle, 'you understand?' He moved on, saying. 'In three—four minutes you will be at his office.'

They drove through the main street of Funchal, past white buildings with balconies, shutters and red roofs. They turned off into a narrow, cobbled side street, turning once again off that. 'There,' the driver said, 'in that shop behind a desk you will find him. That is his headquarters. It is where he runs his taxi service.'

Bewildered, Katherine told herself she should have known that a member of this de Freitas family would always gravitate to the top, 'running' things, organising whatever line of business to which he might choose to devote his life.

As she opened the door, a telephone rang, and then another. Horacio lifted two receivers at once, yet still managed to smile at her in his big, welcoming way. Jorge, his son, was seated behind another desk, twisting a pencil and smiling shyly at her.

Katherine went across to him. 'Jorge,' she said, speaking quietly so as not to interrupt Horacio's two conversations at once, 'I'm longing to see the island, but I don't know about the public transport. Are there buses or——'

'There is no need for you to go anywhere by bus,' Jorge answered, slightly shocked, 'when there are all of my father's taxis at your disposal. Or one of Cousin Luis's own cars, with a driver, any time you want.' His face lit up. 'But I would love to take you to any place you want to see——'

His father's voice, speaking sharply in Portuguese,

interrupted him. Then a telephone rang, Jorge's this time. He answered and even with his father still talking in the background, Katherine could hear the note of puzzlement in Jorge's voice.

'Yes, she is here,' Jorge stated, switching to English, 'do you want to speak to her?' He handed over. 'Your husband.'

Katherine took the receiver, gripping it hard. 'Why do you keep checking on me? You want to know what I'm doing here? Like water, I'm finding my own level.'

There was a crash on her ear and she realised he had cut off.

Her verbal attack had been a defensive measure. Despite her defiance of him from the moment she had discovered his true identity, she was secretly afraid of his power over her. Her love for him was the set of strings, she the puppet and he her puppet-master. All the same, she vowed that, even if it left her in a crumpled heap on the ground, she would cut those strings one day. Power over her Luis might have, but he didn't love her, that she knew for sure. Hadn't he told her he had only married her to have a permanent woman in his life?

Her lips were pressed together to stop them trembling, She turned away, only to turn back when she discovered another man had come in and taken a seat at the empty desk. He, too, was speaking quietly into his telephone. It must, she concluded, be a thriving business which Horacio de Freitas owned.

'Katherine?' Horacio said her name gently. 'Are you upset? Is my nephew treating you badly?' This he said with a smile. 'Come in here, where we can talk.' He led her into a smaller room with a table and three or four chairs. There was a sink and cups and in the air the aroma of coffee, mixed with still-lingering cigarette smoke.

'Now tell me,' Horacio suggested, dusting a chair for her, 'why two intelligent, happy, newly-married people should have quarrelled so soon after coming to this beautiful island of ours.'

Responding to his earnest encouragement, Katherine confessed, 'If you really would like to know——'

'I want to know everything which affects the happiness of my brother's son, and my brother's son's wife. Luis now has no father. His stepmother has not returned with him—which I think was very tactful of her. So I must help all I can, in their place, to keep the happiness in my nephew's marriage. Have you quarrelled, Katherine?'

'It was more a difference of opinion, Mr—Senhor—I mean Uncle——'

'Horacio. Let's leave out the "uncle", shall we?' He frowned. 'Was it this "private conflict" Luis spoke about yesterday when you arrived? And this strange thing—luxury hotels being "against your principles"?'

Hesitantly, hoping she would win his understanding, Katherine told Horacio about her first meeting with Luis, how she had thought him in financial need, about the loan and—she blushed a little, but Horacio laughed—about the condition she had imposed. She told him also about how her mother had left her father because he had neglected her, working all hours of the day, and sometimes the night.

'So it runs in the family,' Horacio commented, smiling, 'this hatred of too much money?'

'Of its corrupting influence,' Katherine put in firmly and Horacio's brown eyes rounded.

'She speaks so politically, so seriously of such matters.' He shook his head. 'In this wonderful island climate of ours, we are so busy living and earning that living we have no time to philosophise. And you,' his hand touched hers fleetingly 'a lovely young bride, should not trouble your head about such things. Think only about making your husband happy, about the children you will have one day——'

He stopped as Katherine shook her head vigorously. 'It's not just principles, Horacio, it's a deep-down conviction. But,' her voice dropped, then rose again to speak over the noise of constantly ringing telephones in the shop, 'it's not only that. Luis let me believe he really needed my money. He let me go on believing it, even after we were married. He acted a lie. I can't forgive him for tricking me. And my father conspired with him.'

It was then that she told him how often her father had tried to persuade her to marry a rich man, and how each time she had rebelled, finally moving away. Then, she told him, he had pretended that Aunt Olga's stepson was poor when compared with the other men she had met— whereas she had now discovered he was in fact richer than all of those other men put together. 'Now,' she finished, 'I feel trapped. I *am* trapped—in a loveless marriage.'

Horacio frowned. 'It cannot be so, Katherine. I am sure Luis had his own reasons for marrying you. Maybe,' his eyes twinkled, 'he had fallen in love?'

Katherine shook her head. 'It was the other way round, Horacio. I fell for him. He only married me because he wanted a woman in his life—he told me.'

Horacio sighed, looking sad. 'You must make him a good wife, Katherine. You offered yourself to him in marriage. He was honourable and accepted you. You must make the best of what you have done. You cannot leave him.' He gave a short laugh at the strangeness of the situation. 'Most women, as Luis said yesterday, would be throwing their arms round his neck for turning suddenly into a near-millionaire. But you——' again he shook his head, 'have to be different.'

For a few minutes he sat, hand to chin, elbow on table, quietly thinking. He muttered something in Portuguese, adding in English, 'A strange twist of fate.' He did not explain himself. His telephone rang, but he ignored it, saying, 'We will return to the shop and I will answer it there. Jorge,' he addressed his son across the shop, 'you offered to take Katherine around the town.'

Jorge nodded eagerly, but his father lifted a hand, listening to the caller. 'Yes, Luis, she is still here. We, she and I, have had a long discussion. But the problem is yours, and hers, to solve. Luis, your wife is a woman to be proud of.' He smiled. 'She has principles. *Qûe?* You didn't marry her for her principles?' He laughed. 'You wouldn't be the man I know you are if you did. You say she must return to the hotel for lunch? I will tell Jorge. He is taking her round. He will look after her. *Até logo.* See you later.'

Jorge pointed out the attractive inlaid pavements, the rows of jacaranda trees down the centre of the wide street. He pointed to the flowers which were growing everywhere. 'Frangipani,' he said, 'or pagoda tree. Kapok tree. They use that, as you probably know, as filling for cushions and things.' Bougainvillea spilled over walls, its flowers white or purple or red.

They drove up narrow, cobbled sidestreets, down again, avoiding the bullock carts which pulled laughing tourists, the bullocks' keepers bending now and then to grease the cart's rails with a cloth.

There was the Governor's Palace, a handsome white buidling with soldiers on guard. Jorge gestured towards the ocean, indicating the quay and the harbour.

'Over there,' he said, 'is where the cruise liners dock. When they come in, my father goes, with many others, to the quay and spreads out the embroidery and craft work made by the people who work for him. The liners' passengers buy the goods and my father keeps some of the money, passing a percentage of it on to the workers.'

Katherine's eyes grew bright at the way Luis's Uncle Horacio did business. It was much closer to her comprehension and beliefs than her husband's or her father's.

Jorge took her back to the hotel. As she thanked him and waved him off, she decided that soon she would take a walk round Funchal, looking in all the shops they had driven past, maybe buying some things to take back home. Then she realised that now she was married to Luis de Freitas, this was her home. There was no going back—anywhere.

Knowing the time at which the meal was served, Jorge had returned Katherine in good time for her to change. As she entered, smiling at the bowing door-keeper who recognised her at once, she marvelled at the size of the reception area.

Dark green tiles shone where the sunlight flooded in through the glass. There were two or three shops, some selling souvenirs and handicrafts, others essentials such as suntan lotion. Plants with bright flowers grew in large tubs placed in corners. At the far end, the wall was made entirely of glass.

Katherine wandered towards it and saw that a spiral staircase wound down to a swimming pool. This was surrounded by tiles, large, multi-coloured sunshades, white tables and seats. Waiters carrying trays of drinks wove their way through the stretched-out sunbathers. Beyond the pool there were gardens. Flowers and flowering trees were everywhere.

Turning from the enticing view, Katherine noticed that photographs were displayed on the walls. She assumed there was a photographic service and the pictures were of guests, past and present. In a corner a young man sat on a stool, an easel and board in front of him. He was painting a woman guest and she was doing her best to stay still.

'Katherine!' At the sound of Luis's voice, she found herself turning automatically. It's as if he's got hypnotic powers, she thought irritably, the way I dance to his tune, respond to his slightest command.

'We'll lunch together,' he informed her. 'Stay in our suite until I come.' His brown eyes gazed unreadably at her. An air of authority, which her own father's ramrod-straight back had always conveyed, was plainly displayed in Luis's whole bearing. Like her father, also, he expected to be obeyed. The years, however, had matured her father, making him more tractable. He had learnt to handle his daughter with a coaxing subtlety.

Not so her new husband, whose arrogance had only surfaced on arriving on his own home ground. Where she, his wife, was concerned, she doubted if the words 'coax' or 'persuasion' were in her vocabulary. What if she rebelled against his autocratic manner?

'Suppose I don't want to lunch with you?' she challenged, walking towards him. 'I might just want to drink by the pool.'

'Right.' A lift of his broad shoulders. 'We'll have that drink by the pool. Then we'll go and eat.'

Katherine swung away, making for the lift. Luis must have motioned to the porter, since he was there before her, his fingers on the button. The lift arrived quickly, almost as if it knew it had been summoned on the owner's behalf. The bellboy stared down and took her silently up to the floor he knew she wanted.

Using the key the receptionist had handed her as she had talked to Luis, Katherine let herself in, crossing the lounge area. Then she stood, astonished, as she saw the rail on wheels which had been pushed into the main bedroom. From it hung dresses, gowns, elegant evening blouses and skirts, even slacks and new jeans, complete with tee-shirts and tops.

There was a movement behind her and she swung to see her husband standing a pace or two away. His face was without expression, his head lowered slightly as if daring her to revolt against his act of ordering clothes for her without her consent.

She ran the back of her hand carelessly along the clothes, lifting her head and giving him a brilliant smile. 'For me? Darling, how kind!' She was, she hoped, at that moment every inch the 'rich man's daughter'. Way back she had learnt the role, but it had grown rusty with disuse. On leaving home and finding herself rooms in a shabby shared house, she had deliberately shed that skin. Now the knowledge of how to play the rich girl—even the rich man's wife—was proving surprisingly useful.

If she had hoped to confuse him and wonder bewilderedly whether his rebel of a wife had decided at last to play ball and accept his elevated status in society, she had hoped wrongly. The only gauge to his reaction was the faint hardening of his already flint-hard eyes.

'But I'm sorry, darling, they're so obviously not my style, I'm not even going to try them on.' Walking to the bed and flinging down her bag, she braced herself for his angry assault on her body. It did not come and she turned large, innocent-looking eyes in his direction. 'You might as well send them back to wherever they came from. You see,' she strolled to face him glad that a human body was not transparent that he couldn't see her heart beating madly, 'I refuse to act the part of the exalted, opulent owner's wife.'

Her fingers were straightening his tie, brushing a lapel. She knew she was playing with fire. 'Keep it up, my love,' Luis drawled. 'You may not know it, but you are already perfect in that part.' His hand pressed over hers. 'You're also seducing me, *amada*. And if it were not time to eat, I would be responding to your seduction with every weapon I possess.' He lifted her hand away. 'Go and change. We'll eat in the grillroom.'

Katherine put a distance between them. 'I'm not changing, Luis. I'm staying just as I am. If you're too ashamed to be seen with me in these simple clothes, then we'll lunch separately.'

He scrutinised her for a few moments, and his look aroused in Katherine both defiance and uncertainty. As his wife, her conscience told her, she should want to please him. As the victim of his and her father's trickery, she found her principles urged her to disregard his wishes. Her principles won. 'I'm not changing,' she repeated.

He opened the bedroom door, inviting her to precede him. 'A drink by the pool, you said?' he remarked.

The descent in the lift was silent, but the mirrors around them showed her that he watched every move she made. She fretted under his unrelenting surveillance and tried to return his stare, but her eyes fell away almost at once. The man she had married she could have touched and kissed playfully. This icy person she could not even talk to.

They walked part way down the spiral staircase, made for a bar which led off the stairs and was situated in a wide alcove overlooking the pool. Katherine pushed herself on to a bar stool while Luis stood, one elbow on the counter, waiting while other customers were served.

When eventually the young man behind the bar saw him, he did not seem to recognise his new customer. Katherine stared, first at the barman, then at her husband, expecting to see at least a frown of annoyance, but there was only a lurking smile of amusement, as if he knew she was watching him.

Luis pushed the drink along the counter, having learnt her preferences from the first days of their marriage. He half-sat on a stool and lifted his glass. 'To our wonderful marriage,' he said in a mocking toast, 'may it thrive and blossom into miniature likenesses of myself and you.'

Katherine coloured angrily, her answering look rebellious, but she put the glass to her lips, sealing the toast. I dance to his tune, she thought, ever since we met he's had it his way, even making me fall in love with him, although she had to admit that that was not strictly true. From the start he had disturbed her, with his penetrating brown eyes, his toughness, his innate strength.

Her heart had gone mad at the mere sight of him and she had known he had been the one she'd been looking for. Now the words of his provocative toast stirred feelings of unbearable longing. She wanted to have his children, but first she would have to have his love. And that, she knew, was as impossible as climbing a mountain on roller skates.

Arrows pointed to the seawater pool, the heated pool, the paddling pool. Katherine chose the seawater pool, shaped like an indented circle. There were palm trees here and there, exotic plants provided colour in the sunbathing area.

Choosing a lounger, she shed her towelling top and skirt, leaving them in a pile. Adjusting the shoulder straps of her bronze-coloured two-piece swimsuit, she made for the water's edge. A few people swam, but most were content to lie in the warm sun.

Katherine descended into the blue-tinted, sparkling water, gripping the rail. It had been a long time since she had used a swimming pool. the feel of the water lapping at her shoulders while the sun shone from a cloudless sky was a pleasure she was appreciating the more for having denied herself of it for so long.

For some time she swam, clambering out at last and shaking the water from her hair. She looked up to find a man standing a short distance in front of her, smiling in a pleasant, if slightly familiar way. Her smile in return was brief, displeased rather than flattered by his appreciative gaze. His polite 'excuse me' made her realise that she was blocking his way to the steps. Apologising with a smile, Katherine stepped aside, but the man did not move.

'Hi,' he said, 'enjoying your vacation?'

There was no need to tell him that for her it was not just a vacation but a lifetime. 'Fine,' she answered. 'You, too?'

'Oh, me, I work here.'

Katherine frowned. She remembered seeing him somewhere before. There was a faint intonation in his speech which made her ask, 'Are you American?'

'I sure am, and proud of it. But I've been here a few years. Worked at this hotel for most of them.'

Katherine noted his pushed-back fair hair, the easiness of his manner, and wondered where in the building he was employed. Reception? Then she remembered. 'In the entrance foyer—painting people!'

'Right. That's my job and I love it. Money's good too. It's handed over to the management, but I get a pretty good commission. Want to have your portrait painted, ma'am?' He smiled broadly. 'You'd make a darned good subject.'

Something drew her eyes towards the building. From one of those hundreds of windows eyes were watching her. She didn't know which window, but she took an inspired guess as to whose eyes they were.

'I'd love to,' she answered, giving the young man the benefit of her wide smile, 'some time before long.'

His hand went out to hold her chin and he studied her face. 'Fascinating features, large eyes. Look, I'm free this evening. Would you——'

Katherine was already shaking her head. This man was practised in the art of flattery. He had to be, in his line. But eyes were boring into her and the possessor of those eyes could make life very unpleasant for her if she encouraged any man, let alone an employee. The man's job might even be at risk.

Swiftly she moved away. 'I don't know your name——'

'Dan,' he supplied, 'Dan Stewart.'

'Dan, I'm Katherine de Freitas. Senhor de Freitas—

Luis—is my husband.'

Dan seemed to pale under his suntan. He put a hand to his forehead. 'Well, I'll be——!' He moved towards the steps, turning to descend backwards. 'Pardon me, Mrs de Freitas, but I think I'd better get under——' with his foot he indicated the pool water, 'before I get pushed under, if you get my meaning.' With a splash he was gone.

Katherine returned to her lounger, towelling herself, then stretching out to sunbathe. Lazily she rubbed lotion on her arms and legs, but the sun was not burning down, just shining with a deep luxuriating warmth. Her eyes roamed and she watched the palm trees sway in the gentle breeze in the gardens adjoining the swimming pool area.

Dan Stewart came past after his swim and she smiled as he lifted a hand in greeting. She smiled again when he had gone, noticing the unnecessary distance he had put between them. It seemed that he, as well as she, was concerned about keeping his job at the hotel.

People were collecting their belongings and moving. Her watch told her it was time for tea and she pulled on her towelling top and skirt, gathered her things and, pattering in her sandals, returned through the glass doors. Climbing the spiral steps, she met her husband at the top. If his mood could be judged by his expression, then it was not good.

'Tea will be served in our suite,' he announced, blocking her way. 'I would prefer that you had it there.'

'Why?' she challenged. 'Don't you like me mixing with the hotel's employees?'

'Mix with them as much as you like, but don't let them maul you. Do you understand?'

People were appearing at the bottom of the spiral steps and straggling upwards. Luis took her arm and led her across the reception area, behind the counter and through a door. They passed through a large office where a number of young women were working, through another

door into a room at which a woman sat alone at a type-
writer, then into a room of enormous size with a view
both to the front and the rear of the building.

The whole office suite was palatial, and it was then
that the truth hit Katherine full in the face. She had
married a man who was even more fanatically work-
motivated than her father. And that, she thought with
dismay, she had never believed possible.

'All this,' she said, indicating the scattered couches and
armchairs, the fitted carpeting, the chrome and glass
tables, the pot plants, 'to run the Hotel Sereno.'

'Not entirely,' Luis was standing hand in pockets,
lounging against the side of his desk. His eyes were busy
noting her slightly unruly appearance, the length of thigh
and leg which showed beneath the short towelling skirt. 'I
run my other business from here, too.'

'What other business?' Her wide eyes were not smiling
now.

'Exporting—wines, embroideries, crafts, a banana exporting business. I share with Horacio a banana plantation, vineyards.'

With a hand to her head, Katherine sought and found
the comfort of a chair. He stayed where he was and it was
as though the distance between them spanned the world,
not merely halfway across a room.

Her pale face lifted. 'I married a poor man, but he
turned into you. I'm not your wife, I'm his.' Her voice
lowered. 'I loved him. I want a divorce from you.'

His smile was a slash across his mouth. His eyes sparkled
like the sun on the sea, without its warmth. It was a glitter
not of pleasure, but a muted fury. 'I'm one man, not two,
and it was I you married, Kate. You are mine in every
sense of the word. You stay mine. There will be no
divorce.'

CHAPTER SEVEN

IT was evening and the setting sun had lowered beyond the horizon, leaving its brilliance behind in an orange and gold array of colour mixed with deepening blue clouds sweeping gloriously across the sky.

The blue of the sea had changed, too, reflecting back the sunset shades. Lights from the shore, from lighted streets and floodlit hotels poured out and down to the water as if to watch themselves competing with Nature's own paintbox tints and tones.

Katherine stood, fascinated, at the window leading to the balcony. In the bedroom the rail of clothes still stood, as if awaiting her attention. That, she thought rebelliously, they would not get.

The door opened and she turned to watch Luis enter. His hand went to his tie and he pulled at it, removing it. His jacket followed and he stretched in a low chair, closing his eyes. So he was tired. She would not, could not, let her longing to run to him show. Any weakness in her armour that she displayed he would see and work on relentlessly.

'Is our marriage tiring you?' she asked, quietly taunting.

He was not provoked. His eyes stayed closed. 'Our marriage? It hasn't even begun.'

'It has, it has!' She might not have aroused him, but he had succeeded in arousing her. 'It began—and ended—back in my home, my threadbare, worn-out flat. We were alive there, Luis, we were happy. Don't you remember?'

Why was she pleading, she asked herself angrily, pleading to save a marriage which was finished?

Hadn't she just told him?

'I remember,' he answered drowsily, 'I remember.' There was a long pause. 'I played it your way then.' Another pause, then, as she watched, his muscles stiffened and he was out of the chair like a tensed tiger springing. 'Now you'll play it mine. Those dresses,' he indicated the rail, 'try them on. Give me a private fashion show.' His sardonic smile goaded her.

'I won't!' She made for a door, any door. It happened, unluckily, to be the glass door to the balcony, but she pushed through and stood, back to the rail, gripping it behind her.

Luis went towards her, but stayed in the doorway, propped there, his arms folded. 'Where do you think you're going?' he asked lazily. 'It's twelve floors down. I'd advise you to take the lift—it's safer.'

She was cornered, and when he straightened and made for her, she grew taut. When he reached her, she would dodge—then his fingers were round her arms. 'You'd prefer that I undressed you? My love, I'll gladly——'

'No!' With a backward jerk she was free, but the blow across her back from the balcony rail hurt her spine so much she took a ragged breath and sagged, bending to prevent a faint.

Giving her a few moments, Luis lifted her upright. His arms went round her and she clung to him, she could not stop herself. His hand massaged her back and he was so gentle she nearly cried. It was shock, she told herself, not a weakness in her defences. He would do the same for anyone who had been stupid enough to do what she had done.

He walked her through the communicating door to the living area, seated himself in a chair and pulled her on to his lap. She lay there quiescent, content, her eyes closed to the luxury around her, and thought about the recent past. If only wishes had the dreamlike quality of a magic carpet and could waft the wisher where they wanted to go!

'I'd go back to our beginning,' she murmured to herself, 'and trap us in a time bubble. Then there'd just be the two of us together for always, never changing.'

Her head lifted and his hand stopped massaging her back. If only she could tell this remote man who was her husband, yet a stranger, that the pain wasn't really there. It was a perpetual ache which held her body in bondage, never loosening its grip.

Fiercely her eyes searched his, but she could find no chink in his armour. Even when he met her gaze and smiled, there was no love in it, only a thinly-veiled amusement. Nor even when his lips met hers and his hand rested familiarly on her thigh did he reveal that the contact sprang from anything other than his male reflexes.

He did not seem to have heard her words, although she knew he had. His choosing to ignore them annoyed her and she struggled from his lap, straightening her sleeveless dress. 'Is the pain better now?' he asked, as detached as a doctor. When she nodded, he said, 'Good, now try on those dresses.'

She thought he had forgotten! What would he do, she wondered, if she did not move? Two seconds later, she knew the answer. He was unfastening the buttons, removing her dress. Two small wisps of clothing were left. He made as if to remove them, but she backed away. His actions already had her pulses dancing like a primitive tribe preparing to celebrate a ritual sacrifice.

He had won, but then he always did. But the 'sacrifice'—herself—was not going to give in without a fight. 'You certainly know how to undress a woman,' she taunted. 'Just like a rich man and his mistress.'

Luis gazed at her, unmoved.

'The first night I met you,' she went on, 'I said you thought like a rich man, and that was before I knew the truth about you. I noticed that you tipped people like a rich man, too.' She wrapped her arms about herself. Although the evening was warm, she had unaccountably begun to shiver. 'My instinct made me afraid even before we left—afraid to come here with you.'

'Which reveals your wonderful insight into future happenings,' he sneered. 'You should have listened to your "instinct", shouldn't you?'

Even though her lip was trembling, her large hazel eyes stared at him belligerently. He went to her, removed her arms and put his own around her waist. His glance rested on the inviting cleft revealed by her low-cut bra. Then he stilled her lip with his thumb.

'You keep talking of our first days together. Katherine, they've gone. You said you loved the man I was then, implying that you no longer love the man I am now. I'm both, *amada,* two in one. You must learn to accept it.'

'And if I don't?'

Broad shoulders lifted expressively. 'Too bad for you. Look at it this way, truthfully. You were infatuated by a dream, an image, a male creature fashioned by a—shall we say, a draughtswoman—yourself—on the drawing board of your imagination.'

'If so, can I really be blamed? You and my father connived against me. If I'd known the truth then, you have my word for it that I wouldn't be here now.'

Again the shoulders shrugged. He let her go, walking back into the bedroom. Katherine scooped up her dress and followed. He was looking through the dresses. 'This first,' he ordered, giving her a gown of shell-pink velvet.

Taking it from his arm, Katherine held it up to assess its style, then put it against her, looking at her reflection. Its delicate shade suited her colouring. Quickly, before he could do it for her, she pulled it over her head and found that its fit was perfect.

He turned her, looked her over and nodded. His palms

skimmed her bare arms, rested against her back which the low cut of the gown left uncovered. He ran a careless finger along the revealing rounded neckline. 'Now the others,' he commanded.

There was an oyster silk gown which hid nothing of her shape, a jacket and matching skirt in blue, sundresses, slacks and casual blouses. After the third dress, his appraisal, his half-mocking attitude at her increasing annoyance as he insisted she displayed each garment as if she were a model, stirred her defiance to life and action.

'That's all I'm trying on now,' she asserted, and reached for her own dress.

He caught her and clamped his arms around her, using his lips to bring an end to her struggles. 'You talk of mistresses,' he muttered against her neck, and she shivered under the feathering touch of his mouth, 'but *you* are my mistress, *querida*. Who would want another woman with you as a lover?'

'Luis, Luis,' she heard herself whispering, 'why can't it be like it was before?'

His reaction was to put her roughly from him and walk into the dressing-room. 'Wear the velvet this evening,' he called over his shoulder. 'Occasionally I mix with the guests, meet them, talk to them, sometimes buy them a drink. Tonight I want you with me.' He turned, removing his shirt, and she saw again the inherent strength in him, felt it not only in his physical build but also in the power of his mind.

It was, she knew, useless to prevaricate or refuse, so she used her only weapon—sarcasm. Facing him she said, 'I see you've adopted the habit of the monied classes.' A lifted eyebrow invited her to continue. 'Using a separate dressing-room from your wife. Back at home, in my place, we dressed, undressed, even—even bathed together. Here, conformity is everything, isn't it? Divided even in marriage.'

He was goaded, no doubt about that. She started backing away, but he made no attempt to touch her. 'You swam in the pool this afternoon.' She nodded. 'When I saw you, I was surprised. I imagined you would at least demand to have the water changed so that you wouldn't be contaminated by the water used by those affluent guests.'

So he had decided to meet sarcasm with sarcasm. He went into the shower-room which opened off the dressing-room, locking the door. If anything was a 'keep out' signal, that was it. Katherine's fingers trailed the soft velvet of the dress as it lay across the chair. Why, she wondered dejectedly, was she sarcastic towards him when all she really wanted to do was to hold him close?

The gown suited her in every way. His taste was excellent. How had he known what would suit her? After applying a light covering of make-up, she felt her bare throat. The diamond necklace—it would be a perfect addition, lending its sparkle to the velvet's soft glow.

The box was not in the drawer. Pushing aside the clothes, her fingers searched frantically. 'It isn't there,' she said, 'yet I know I put it here. My necklace,' she addressed Luis who had come to stand at the doorway of the smaller bedroom, 'it's gone!' Shaking fingers pressed into her white cheeks.

He seemed quite unworried. 'Why fret?' he responded. 'You accepted it against your will. To you, it only represents the baubles of a rich man's spoilt wife. It's a label you refuse to have pinned on you, so what does it matter if it's lost?'

Katherine turned on him. 'You gave it to me, don't you understand? You gave——' She realised just how much of herself she had given away to him, but he regarded her coolly.

'It's not been stolen,' he told her tonelessly, shrugging into his jacket. 'We'll collect it from the hotel safe on the way to the restaurant.' He looked her over, his eyes narrowed and assessing. 'You look beautiful.' His tone robbed the words of emotion.

In his room in the suite of offices, he took the necklace from its box and indicated that she should go to him. He looked so handsome in his formal clothes, his air so commanding she wanted to hurry, not stroll as she forced herself to do.

The brush of his fingers on the back of her neck sent minor shock waves racing over her skin. He turned her to face him and his half-smile warned her of the provocative words to come. 'I'm glad you asked me to marry you,' he declared softly.

Katherine jerked free of the hands on her shoulders, but he caught her wrist and forced her to walk beside him. His hand slid down to hold hers and they walked thus into the restaurant. Soft lighting shed its golden glow on to the diners. Spacious windows had been partially curtained by bronze-coloured woven fabric. Through the narrow gaps the restless sea, gilded, like the dining area, with the lowering sun, could be glimpsed.

They were met, as usual, by the head waiter. Luis conversed with him briefly in Portuguese and the man nodded, as if comprehending entirely. They were led not, as Katherine had expected, to a secluded table for two. The head waiter said to the young couple who occupied a table for four,

'Pardon me, *senhor*, *senhora*, but would you object if Senhor and Senhora de Freitas joined you this evening? Or are you expecting friends?'

The couple, whose names were Tom and Ena White, said they would be very pleased to have company and, when Katherine and Luis were seated, they added hadn't they heard the name de Freitas somewhere before?

Katherine looked to Luis to answer, but he seemed in no hurry to enlighten them. Katherine risked her husband's displeasure by suggesting to the guests, 'The hotel leaflet, maybe? On the first page, underneath the hotel's name?'

'That's it!' Ena White exclaimed. 'That's the name of the owner.'

She glanced at her husband, who ventured, 'Any relation to him?'

Again Katherine sought for a response in Luis, but there was none, so she answered bodly, 'This is Luis de Freitas—my husband, he's the owner.'

The woman coloured with embarrassment, while her husband stared. Katherine could sense an increase in tension and this time looked pointedly at Luis, silently urging him to put them at their ease.

'I make a point,' Luis said at last, 'of meeting as many of my guests as possible when I am here. I don't hide my identity when I talk to them. If my wife had not explained, I would have done. But I still like to hear my guests complaints, if they have any, and do my best to put them right.'

'Oh, Mr de Freitas,' Ena exclaimed, 'it's a wonderful hotel. And we mean that, don't we, Tom?'

Her husband nodded vigorously. 'And it's not too expensive, either. We'd saved up a certain amount——'

'It took us months,' his wife interrupted.

'And,' Tom continued, 'we thought it wouldn't be nearly enough, but the travel agent advised us to stay at the Hotel Sereno. She said it catered for people who weren't rich, although it had facilities for people with more money, too.'

'So we came here,' Ena finished, 'thinking it was a kind of first and second class arrangement. But we aren't barred from anything or anywhere, although we didn't pay as much as others.'

Luis withdrew his eyes from his wife's face, which he had been watching with a mocking smile and nodded to his guest. 'Those who pay more have more attention in their rooms—or suites, as most of them have. Things like that.'

They chatted through dinner and Katherine had heard the life stories of Tom and Ena White, plus many of the other guests with whom they had come into contact.

'Is this the only hotel you own, Mr de Freitas?' Tom asked over coffee, which they had chosen to be served at table.

Luis shook his head. 'About three in Portugal, other European countries, too. We're considering expanding our hotel business to the North American continent.'

'Really? In that case,' she laughed at her husband, 'we'll get details and stay in them all!'

Laughing, Luis stood behind his wife's chair and they left two happy guests behind them. He took his wife's hand and when she said, with a touch of anger, 'You didn't tell me that,' he ignored her words and pulled her behind him.

He stopped at a table for two occupied by tanned young women. Again, they were British and responded with eagerness when he explained who he was. 'We saved up for a whole year, my sister and I,' one of them said, 'and honestly it's been worth every penny.'

'Lovely holiday,' the other girl agreed.

Luis took Katherine from table to table. Only a handful seemed sufficiently wealthy to have booked suites with the intention of staying at the hotel for two or three months, as indeed some of them were doing. Other guests, the majority, had made sacrifices for the pleasure of visiting the island and had especially selected that hotel for their stay.

That evening they did not dance. As Luis walked with Katherine to the reception area she said, 'I guess you've been proving a point this evening.'

He inclined his head. 'That all my guests aren't laden

down with the wealth you love to hate? It was something I thought you needed to know.'

'Maybe I did,' she conceded grudgingly, 'but it doesn't alter my attitude. Nothing can erase the way I was tricked about your true status.'

He shrugged, dismissing the subject, telling her he would join her soon in their suite.

'Why, where are you going?' she demanded. 'Out to the casino to spend some of your fabulous wealth? All those hotels—no wonder you're a millionaire! Or,' she was forced to speak softly, as people were passing them all the time, 'are you going to turn playboy and find yourself a more amenable female companion than I am?'

'Say much more, hellcat, and I will!' His face had paled as his anger rose. 'I have a small piece of work to finish, then I'll join you.'

'You're going to *work*?' Firmly she held her deep disappointment in place. It materialised as defiance. 'I shall ...' Her eyes swung around the wide, tiled area, and she saw the resident artist seated in his usual place. He had no clients at that moment. 'I shall have my portrait painted.'

'You do that,' Luis returned coldly. 'But keep a distance between you. No mauling as you allowed him to do this morning.'

'You're deliberately exaggerating. He didn't *maul* me, he just held my face to try and read it. He looked at me with an artistic eye.'

Luis's answering look was sardonic, then he left her, making for his office suite. Katherine strolled to the young man called Dan Stewart. When he saw her he rose, smiling eagerly. 'Why, hallo again. Want your portrait painted, *senhora*?' he joked.

'Yes, please,' Katherine replied simply, and seated herself on the chair.

Dan stared. 'You don't mean it? You mean he—

he——' Dan indicated the administrative offices behind reception, 'he wouldn't mind? He won't fire me?'

'Just as long as you don't touch me,' she answered primly, then burst into laughter.

'Touch you, honey—I mean, *senhora*? Chance would be a fine thing! The owner's wife! This'll make my day—and my career! I'll do it for nothing. Tell him, hon—*senhora*.' He grinned at his near slip. 'Hell, I can't keep calling you that.'

'Call me Katherine. That's my name.'

He dug the air with a paintbrush, jabbing it towards the offices. 'He won't mind?'

'Too bad if he does. Now, paint, will you, Dan? I'm tired and——'

'Here I go. Just keep as still as you can, in that—no, this position.' He went to touch her, but whistled at himself, saying, 'Down, Dan, to heel!' and indicated the required position with his hands.

Half an hour later, there were the beginnings of a half-length portrait in watercolours on his easel. 'This one I can take my time over, put real good finishing touches. Maybe one day it'll find its way on the walls of the boardroom.'

Katherine laughed, as indeed she had been doing for most of the time he had been painting. His amusing remarks had prevented her from being selfconscious.

'Katherine?' Luis voice rang out across the foyer. 'I've completed my work.'

'Whew, her master's voice,' Dan muttered, then aloud and in his most polished manner, 'Thank you, *senhora*, for your patronage. The painting will be finalised some time tomorrow.'

'No hurry,' Katherine assured him. 'I shall be here for a long, long time.'

Dan looked at her curiously, but said nothing.

In their suite, Katherine confronted Luis. 'I can't get

over it—all those hotels! If I'd known who was marrying me, I'd have—I'd have run a million miles from you.' She looked around, noting that the dresses had been put away.

He caught her shoulder and swung her round. 'You know what you are? An ungrateful little bitch. How many women would have given their all to marry a millionaire?'

'I did give my all,' she answered quietly. 'All my money, all my body, all my——' Just in time, she stopped. *Love.* That was the last thing he wanted from her.

Luis let her go and walked to the window, staring out at the night's splendour, moon shimmering on the sea, the lights of Funchal adding their own charm.

'Do you really own them all?' she enquired.

'Yes, but there's a board of management, of course.' His voice had gone flat. 'I'm the president of the company. Horacio's a member of the board. He draws a salary.' He turned, his smile twisted. 'Yes, Horacio, the man you seem to have taken to your heart because of his simplicity, his hard work—it may interest you to know that he's a rich man, too.'

Her gaze fell away from his. 'He—he doesn't behave like one.' His words had disconcerted her.

'He works hard. Okay, so I work hard, very hard, all hours, as you've just discovered. But because his affluence doesn't show on him as mine does on me—it's part of my stock-in-trade, isn't it?—and with your strange worship of the "underdog", you place him over me on your scale of values.'

Katherine shook her head, a sudden tightening of her chest heralding tears that must not fall. 'You lied to me, Luis.'

He was facing her in two strides, hands clamped to her shoulders, shaking her. 'I did not lie to you,' he muttered through clenched teeth.

'You did,' she hit back, despite the punishment, 'you

admitted you didn't succeed in running your late father's business as well as he did.'

He stopped shaking her, but already her head had begun to throb. His hands stayed on her shoulders, gripping savagely. 'Oh no, that I did not do. My stepmother answered that, not I.'

'So Aunt Olga connived with you and my father!'

'If she did, it was only in your—and my—best interests, or so she thought.'

'You did nothing to enlighten me about the true state of your business affairs,' she whispered, her face pale with the pain of his grip. 'You acted a lie, Luis. I can't forgive you for that. I've tried, but—— Anyway,' she diverted, 'you only married me to get a permanent woman in your life. You said so.'

At last he released her, turning away. 'Get ready for bed,' he said expressionlessly, and went into the smaller bedroom.

Lying there, she feigned sleep. When he joined her at last, she went with the movement of the bed, as though relaxed, but her whole body was as tense as stretched elastic.

His hand on her shoulder turned her, and she went round stiffly. 'Take this off,' he ordered, slipping her nightdress from one shoulder. Mechanically she obeyed him. The sight of his body, as naked as hers, was sufficient to set her heart pounding. Yet resentment kept her limbs rigid and unwelcoming.

'Come to me, Kate.' His voice, heavy with the husky charm she could not resist, was almost her undoing, but her brain repeated the words she had used to him—*you acted a lie*. Well, she would act a lie, too. She would pretend she did not love him. If he took her, she vowed, she would be so indifferent and lifeless, he would find no pleasure in using her.

In the end, under his caressing hands and possessive

lips, she had to clench her teeth to stop herself from responding. When his lips teased her breasts, she strangled a cry of joy at his arousal and lay unresponsive beneath him. He paused, his breathing deep as if controlling anger.

'Would you rather I raped you?' he said at last. 'Is that what this frigid doll act is all about?'

'Just go back to being what you were,' she cried at last, 'unsophisticated, ordinary, uncomplicated by things like—like "stock-in-trades" and enormous bank accounts and work, work, work ...' His hands were stroking her body, feathering her hips, his fingertips trailing her thighs. Her head turned from side to side in a mixture of pleasure and a denial of that pleasure. 'I'd love you, then,' she whispered, her head lifting from the pillow, eyes pleading.

'I can't "change", as you call it,' he rasped. 'You'll have to learn to accept me as I am, here, now, beside you.'

'Then I'll hate you, hate you!' she breathed, tearing away from him and curling into a ball.

He uncurled her brutally, leaving scratch marks which bled a little, but he was too enraged to notice in the subdued light. 'It's rape, then,' he snarled, 'and you'll take whatever comes your way!'

He was relentless in his conquest of her, disregarding all her pleas. His hands, his mouth, inflicted a pain which took her beyond the realm of hurt into a blindingly coloured world of strange and tumultuous ecstasy.

Afterwards, her mouth bruised, her body throbbing, she turned her face to the pillow and wept. Luis got out of bed and pulled on a towelling robe, then stood at the window gazing into the darkness. The moon had moved from sight, but its glow lingered faintly on the cresting waves.

Slowly he walked to the bed and Katherine's eyes fluttered open. His expression was beyond her ability to interpret, his eyes equally so, but there was no fear in her now. She was beyond it. As he went from her into the other bedroom, closing the door, she knew that, far from making her hate him, he had inexplicably made her love for him increase far beyond her own powers of understanding.

A breakfast tray was beside the bed when she awoke the following morning. Since everything was covered and the tray electrically heated, Katherine took a quick shower before starting on the food.

The day was bright, although the mountain tops were veiled in mist. The sun-top she chose to wear with a matching blue skirt could be covered if necessary by a cotton jacket.

The food tasted good, the coffee was, as usual, excellent. To her surprise, she discovered that her appetite was equally good. Luis had gone—back to work, she guessed. She wandered into the smaller room and discovered that the bed had been used. It meant, she concluded sadly, that he had not been able to bring himself to sleep beside the woman whom he had, in his own words, raped.

A kind of hopelessness overcame her and she sat, drooping, on the unmade single bed. Why had Luis slept here? she wondered. After the lovemaking – if that was what it could be called – after her total surrender to his every wish and whim, despite the anger inherent in his every touch and caress, had he lost so his respect for her, he could not bear to be near her any more?

The main entrance door to the suite was opened. Katherine assumed it was the room maid and that she was collecting the breakfast tray. Instead, Luis appeared at the door which linked the main bedroom with the smaller one. In some confusion she stood up, straightening her skirt for something to do.

She had dreaded the moment of their first meeting after the events of the night, but she need not have worried. Luis was back to his normal, aloof self. If he had asked her why she was there, her impulse would have been to say, To get a little nearer to you, but he did not ask the question and she relaxed.

He raked her with dark, unreadable eyes, then caught her gaze as she looked at him. She hoped her face was as blank as his, but she doubted it. He was highly accomplished in the art of the blank face. In his world full of business and board meetings and finance, she guessed it was a valuable asset. It hardly made for a good marriage, though, she reasoned.

'Trying to hide?' was his sarcastic question.

'Hide? From what?' she asked indignantly. 'I wasn't the attacker last night, I was the attacked. You,' she accused, 'treated me like a mistress last night, but I'm your wife, not a passing female. All of which means you don't love me, because a man doesn't love his mistress, just uses her. You used me. So by elimination, it means that there must be a woman somewhere that you do love. Who is she, Luis?'

He rubbed a hand over his jaw. 'Your reasoning has me confused. You've just made two or three questionable statements mixed with a couple of false assertions.' He went towards her, his hands on his hips, jacket draping over them. She wanted to rest her cheek against that broad chest and be gathered in those powerful arms. He stopped a footstep away. 'You—attacked? A peculiar description of a woman who, by her actions and words, couldn't get enough of what I was giving her.'

'There's no need to be crude,' she fumed, hoping her anger covered the despair she was feeling.

'"A man doesn't love his mistress"?' he quoted her. 'Don't make sweeping statements. "There must be another woman somewhere"?' He used her words again.

'Good God, Kate, I'd need to be a superman plus, plus, to have a secret woman *and* you!'

He was laughing at her. Once she would have laughed with him, laughed until she was helpless, wrapped in his arms. The memory of their good days together almost choked her. She pushed past him and went into the main bedroom.

'I'm going out,' she informed him.

'Where?'

'Am I going to be under surveillance again today? Don't worry, I won't leave you—not for a while. I want to see the rest of this beautiful island before I go.'

He dragged her round. 'Sarcastic little bitch!'

No, I'm not, she wanted to shriek, just passionately in love with you and asking for just a bit of love in return.

His fingers were bruising her arm again, but she mal-treated her lip instead of crying out. 'Wherever you go, you'll be watched. I'm not going to be a second Halmar Matthews, deserted by my wife.'

'I'm only going to look round Funchal,' she answered slowly, and his grip eased.

'Do you want an escort?'

'If I do, I'll go to Horacio's.'

'He's not always there.'

'Then I'll go on my own.'

This time she walked out on him, but the spurt of pleasure she experienced at doing so lasted no more than a second.

In the town, she went with the crowds, crossing roads wherever it was possible through the busy traffic, pausing to look in shop windows and glance at cafés. Under her feet she found beautiful patterned black and white mosaic-like pavements.

Along the Avenida Arriaga, purple-flowered jacaranda trees lifted their beauty over the slow-moving traffic. At a road junction stood the impressive statue of the island's founder, João Gonçalves Zarco.

Narrow cobbled streets branched off the main roads. They were steep and often became congested, especially when vehicles were forced to edge past people walking up or down them. Old, balconied houses lined the roads and were a reminder of an elegant age gone by.

Katherine found a café with tables and chairs grouped outside. Seating herself, she asked the waiter for a coffee. Having drunk her fill, she stared around, feeling the life and the movement, the colour and the warmth seeping into her body, becoming part of her.

A taxi drew up at the kerb. Jorge was at the wheel, waving to her. He indicated that he could not stay there, so could she please join him?

At once Katherine was up and across the pavement. 'Please get in,' Jorge invited, and Katherine did so.

'Have you been instructed to watch me?' she asked jokingly, and Jorge turned red. 'You have!' She controlled her temper for his sake and remarked, 'I suppose I've had my hour of freedom and now I've got to return to imprisonment at the hotel?'

Jorge stayed red. 'I don't know what you mean, Katherine.'

Her hand touched his fleetingly. 'Sorry. But—well, there's a disagreement, you see. Between Luis and myself. The hotel—all that luxury, all the money . . .' Katherine took a deep breath. 'I—I was tricked, you see. I wanted the simple life.'

Jorge looked even more embarrassed, if that were possible. 'Is that what Luis meant the other day when we met you at the airport—something about "against your principles"?'

'Yes, yes, that's right.'

Jorge's shoulders lifted. 'Well, you are married to him now, so there is nothing you can do about it.'

'Isn't there?' Katherine commented challengingly, but

Jorge stayed silent. 'Where are we going, Jorge?'

'Have you seen the municipal gardens? Then I will take you there. After that, the market is well worth a visit.'

'I'd like to wander round the craft shops, buy one or two things.'

Jorge nodded. 'Later.' He negotiated the traffic, found a parking place tucked away and escorted her to the gardens. There they strolled for a while, finding a bench and enjoying the green oasis of peace amongst the commerce and bustle of the busy town. Tall palm trees rose from well-tended soil and everywhere were exotic flowers, shrubs and trees.

'You will like the market,' Jorge said as they drove to find a parking place, saying he would wait for her.

Entering the large building, Katherine decided that it reminded her of a kind of Victorian swimming pool. The women sellers wore shawls and calf-skin boots, the men their woollen caps. Everywhere Katherine looked, there were greengrocers' stalls. The place was noisy and crowded and now and then she was pushed away from where she wanted to go.

Upstairs there was a balcony, again crammed with stalls selling fruit and vegetables. The light was not bright and the constant bustle added a sense of excitement. The smell of the wares, the fish, the exotic fruits set out on wicker trays, filled her nostrils.

Returning to join Jorge in the taxi, she said she felt hustled and bustled but had enjoyed every minute. He smiled and drove on, showing her the Ribeira de Santa Luzia, one of Funchal's ravines. The river bed was covered with arched trellises over which grew a mass of bougainvillea, a flowering river in itself.

'At certain times of the year,' Jorge explained, 'the great rush of water coming down from the mountains can hardly be contained by the *ribeira*'s walls.' He moved on from the bridge on which they had stopped. 'Now I will show you the sixteenth-century fort along the seafront. It was the first fortification to be built by the Portuguese in Madeira. It is now the Governor's Palace.'

It, was, Katherine discovered, an impressive building, its outer walls a creamy white, the shutters of the windows painted brown. It was large, too, and well guarded.

'Now I must take you back to my father's office,' Jorge said. 'A taxi from the hotel will collect you there.'

'I should love to see your father,' Katherine told him, adding firmly, 'but not yet. I told you, I want to wander round the craft shops.'

'No, no, I have orders——'

'I *won't* be treated by my husband as if I were a criminal on parole, being watched, trailed, directed everywhere!' Her anger cooled as she saw his face. 'I'm sorry, Jorge, I shouldn't involve you in a private quarrel.'

Jorge shook his head bewilderedly. 'Luis is good. He is a fine man. He is much liked here, much admired. You above all, Katherine, should admire him and respect his wishes. He has taken over his father's business and made it even more successful. Don't you appreciate all that he has achieved?' Katherine shook her head. 'But what has he done wrong, Katherine?'

'He's rich.'

'And that is a crime in your eyes?'

'Yes.'

Jorge let out a deep sigh. 'I just do not understand you, Katherine.'

'You don't know the—the background to our meeting and our marriage. Here,' she touched Jorge's arm, 'here will do. I'll walk home. Thanks, Jorge, for the sightseeing. I really enjoyed it. Who's taking over the detective work now you're going?'

He stared at her, then saw her smile. 'As far as I know,'

he laughed, 'you are a free agent.' With a wave, he drove away.

The craft shop she entered was large, and as she wandered round she became conscious of a woman following her. Another private detective on my trail? Katherine wondered. But the woman smiled and Katherine realised she was a saleswoman silently encouraging her to buy. Maybe she could only speak her own language.

At last Katherine stopped wandering and came to a decision about her purchases. There were so many things she wanted, it was as though she were a tourist instead of a resident. Deep inside, she told herself, she felt like a tourist. Something, somewhere in her brain, was telling her that one day she would leave the island ...

'A tea-cosy or two?' the saleswoman asked. Katherine stared. Her English was perfect! 'They still drink tea in England, I'm sure.'

Her hair was a deep brown and caught into a knot behind her head. Her eyes were long-lashed, her mouth wide and smiling. Her clothes were of the best quality and she wore them gracefully. A picture of elegance, Katherine thought, a manner as charming as the smile.... Yet there was something about the woman that pushed away rather than attracted. Katherine simply could not define it.

'Yes, yes, they do,' she answered, hastily filling the silence. 'Always will, I expect. The tea-cosies certainly are lovely—beautiful embroidery, so much colour. The dancing figures look as though they're about to move.' After the spilling out of words, she collected herself. 'I'll have—let me see—three of them, please. And two aprons, a tray cloth. . . .'

By the time she had finished, it was a long list and a large pile awaited her. The woman helped her with the money, counting out sufficient to cover the cost. 'Can I send them anywhere for you?' the saleswoman enquired. 'A house, hotel or——?'

'Hotel, please. That would be fine.'

'You're a tourist. How long will you be staying?' the woman asked conversationally. 'Most people say "not long enough"!'

'For—for some time,' Katherine answered, for some reason not wishing to tell this woman about her private affairs.

'What about you, do you live here?'

'For ten years now. I came with my husband, but he died, so I took this shop over. It's been quite a success.'

'You own it?' The woman nodded. 'Actually bought it?'

'Actually bought it,' the woman answered, laughing, and Katherine felt uncomfortably that it was at her, at her seeming naïveté. 'I borrowed quite a sum of money, then the giver told me there was no need to repay it.'

Other customers wandered in. A young girl assistant went to help them. 'Now,' the owner said, taking a notepad and pencil, 'where do I send your purchases?'

'The Hotel Sereno, please.'

The woman's eyebrows shot up. 'An expensive place, isn't it? Excellent, but——' Her swift appraisal and consequent summing-up of Katherine's social placing implied that she considered such a hotel to be out of her reach. 'Name? And is it urgent?' the woman asked.

'Not urgent,' Katherine replied, adding with a flick of pleasure, 'my stay here is indefinite, permanent in fact.' The woman's brow pleated. 'My name is Senhora de Freitas.'

The woman stared at the notepad, her fingers gripping the pencil so hard they turned white. When her face lifted, that was white too. 'The wife of—Luis de Freitas?'

'Yes,' the lift of Katherine's head was proud, 'I'm Luis de Freitas's wife.' Too sweetly, she asked, 'Why, do you know him?'

The woman's stare was hostile. 'I know Luis. I know him well. He didn't tell me about you.' The hostility receded and a charming smile widened her mouth. 'You must have taken him by storm, as they say. Although you're not—exactly—the type I thought he would—marry.' As the woman had spoken, her glance had again skimmed Katherine's slender figure, as if attempting to readjust her ideas about this customer's social standing.

'You haven't told me your name,' Katherine affirmed, making her tone friendly.

'Delphine,' the woman answered, 'Delphine Evans. Ask Luis—he'll know. Oh, and,' as Katherine turned to go, 'I'll get these items to the hotel as soon as I can.' Katherine thanked her. 'By the way,' Delphine Evans added, her smile growing even more charming, 'that money I told you I borrowed to buy this place—forget I didn't have to repay it, will you?'

CHAPTER EIGHT

KATHERINE walked back to the Hotel Sereno. It took her longer than she had expected because she walked slowly, giving herself time to think. After meeting the woman Delphine Evans, she needed that time—to wonder how it was that she knew Luis, how long she had known him, but most of all how *well* she knew him.

'That money,' the woman had said, 'forget I didn't have to repay it.'

The statement nibbled at her mind, worrying her, reducing her, like a mouse at a piece of cheese. Which was no doubt what the woman had intended. Why hadn't Luis told her about Delphine Evans? But would a man tell his wife about the 'other woman' in his life?

A man doesn't love his mistress? he had quoted back at her. *Don't make sweeping statements,* he'd added. Did it mean that if Luis had had a mistress he had loved her? And was Delphine Evans that woman? Katherine put a hand to her head. When would the questions stop? Never, probably, she decided, nodding automatically to the doorman who saw her into the hotel entrance foyer.

After all, she had proposed to Luis, hadn't she, giving no thought whatsoever to any private relationship he might already have on his Atlantic island home. He had married her—she would probably never know why—but did that necessarily mean he had to sacrifice everything connected with his private life, even the woman he loved?

As she collected her key from reception, the door to Luis's suite of offices was opened. 'Katherine!' It was Horacio standing there, his face all smiles, his arms wide in welcome. 'You have enjoyed your tour of Funchal, with my son's help? He did not make one pass at you, I hope?'

Katherine laughed. 'Jorge was as polite and correct in his attitude as he always is, Horacio. He's a good son—I'm sure you know that.'

'I know that, Katherine. But just to make sure he stays good I have to keep on keeping him in his place. When he is away at Lisbon at university, I am not there to see what he is up to, but if his exam results are bad, I am bad to him!'

Horacio's frown was so fierce, Katherine laughed again. Luis was in the doorway, and his eyes were on his wife's face. A faint, reminiscent kind of smile played about his mouth and it was not, she was sure, Horacio's words which had amused him. A shiver coursed through her as memories returned of their night together.

'Come, Kate,' Luis commanded softly, and his arm moved in a beckoning motion.

Going round the desk, she passed the young woman receptionist whose eyes were firmly on her work. Horacio moved a step back and motioned Katherine, with a sweeping politeness, into her husband's office.

Horacio asked, falsely ingenuous, 'You have mended your foolish quarrel? You love him now?'

'I—I always....' Swiftly she changed her words. 'I always did hate a quarrel.' It would have been true, she thought with some surprise, I always have loved him, even from the moment I saw him.

'Well, do you love me, Kate?' Luis's smile was devilish, goading her. She would not be goaded.

'I'll tell you when we're alone, darling,' she promised, her eyes taking up his challenge.

Horacio's hand lifted. '*Adeus*, Luis. That was a broad hint to your Uncle Horacio to leave. I will take that hint, Katherine.' He bowed, added a smile and left.

'So,' Luis commented when they were alone, 'there's a

disagreement between you and myself. The hotel—all that luxury, all the money. You were tricked, you wanted the simple life. Your principles are offended by the life you're being forced to lead. You're a prisoner at this hotel?'

Katherine's face was white with disbelief. 'How do you know all that? Did Jorge let me down and tell his father? Is that why Horacio was here?'

Luis's shoulders straightened. His hands cupped his elbows. 'Jorge did not tell his father.'

'You used my exact words. So how did you know?' She frowned, thinking hard. 'There's no transmitter or radio receiver in the taxi, so how——? A tape recorder? Hidden somewhere in the dashboard? You wouldn't! You wouldn't stoop to that!'

'I have an intelligent wife.' He slipped a hand into his jacket pocket and drew out a pocket recorder. He pressed a switch and the conversation between Jorge and herself sounded loud and clear. Luis switched off the recorder and placed it on his desk. He went across to a door and opened it, speaking in Portuguese to the occupant of the room.

Katherine heard his secretary's voice answer, '*Sim, senhor.*'

Luis closed the door and strolled back to face his wife. 'I've sent my secretary for her lunch, so you can shriek your head off if that's how you feel.'

'So it was in the car! No wonder Jorge seemed so embarrassed about what I was saying. And Horacio brought it here? Having listened to it first, I suppose?'

'I doubt it. A married couple's quarrels hardly make for exciting listening.'

Katherine felt a storm raging inside her, but after his sarcastic invitation to her to 'shriek' her head off, she held it back with all her strength.

It forced its way through the cracks in her barriers, nonetheless, forming itself into acid words. 'Do you know what?' said Katherine, her eyes reflecting the tumult inside her. 'I'm beginning to hate you.'

'That's news,' Luis interpolated with a bland smile.

'Planting listening devices to monitor my conversation when you're not there, having me followed——' A thought struck her. 'If you know all about my movements, tell me where I went after Jorge left me in the town.'

'I have no idea. You tell me.' His tone was easy, but his eyes were watchful.

Katherine believed then that he really did not know, which meant she need not tell him. And that, she thought, was just as well, since she had not yet decided how much Delphine Evans' claim to know Luis well was motivated by jealousy of herself, his new wife; or whether Delphine really did 'know him well', but only as a friend.

The insinuation about the non-repayment of the loan was, Katherine had decided, added out of malice. After all, hadn't she, Katherine, captured a prize as a husband—a wealthy, handsome, aristocratic kind of man, probably chased by all the eligible and probably ineligible women on the island?

'I just shopped around.' Katherine answered Luis's question with a graceful but casual lift of her shoulders.

Pressing the 'on' button of the pocket recorder, she heard the conversation in the car come hesitantly into the room. The car's engine noise was prominent, but it did not drown the underlying message in the words. She turned to Luis, who was smiling sarcastically.

'You really are despicable,' she asserted. 'I meant every word that recorder picked up. I'm watched, followed, bugged by listening devices.'

'And you're a prisoner?' he goaded.

'Yes, your prisoner. You can't deny it.'

'But I do deny it, *querida*.' His eyes had narrowed and it seemed a thought had occurred to him. He caught her wrist, pulled her to the door, across the reception area towards the swing doors. Many eyes turned on them and Katherine forced herself to walk at Luis's side, since the embarrassment of those puzzled glances was colouring her cheeks.

The doorkeeper opened the swing door and bowed them through.

'Where are you taking me?' Katherine asked through her teeth.

'Exactly nowhere,' was her husband's terse reply. At the top of the steps he halted, lifted her captured wrist and, with a gesture of someone ridding himself of unwanted rubbish, let her go. 'You're free,' he told her, 'free as a bird.' He dusted his hands. 'I have just released you from your so-called imprisonment. You can go. Your luggage will be packed and sent on.'

Reaching into his inner pocket he extracted his wallet, drew out a wad of notes, took her handbag from her and pushed the notes inside. 'All British money. A taxi will take you to the airport. Thanks for the memories. Goodbye, Katherine.'

He strode back into the hotel, leaving her bemused, and not a little afraid, on the steps.

Katherine wanted to turn and run into the hotel. She wanted to snatch back everything that, in a few moments of resentment expressed in a conversation in a taxi, she seemed to have thrown away.

Pride, however, made her walk away from the place. Unable to think of anything else, she walked into the town, pausing as she found the tourist office in front of her. After a few minutes of wandering round the shop looking at leaflets, the assistant offered her booklets which suggested things to do.

Paying for them, she thanked the young woman, saying. 'I think I'll explore some of the island on foot.'

'The *levadas*,' the assistant suggested, 'there are many walks you could do to see them. But they are graded. You see,' she removed a booklet from Katherine's hands, 'the distance, the time they take, it's all here. The *levadas*—they are our system of irrigating the land,' the woman explained. 'It was begun by the early settlers on this island. Once, all the rain that descended over the mountains just ran back into the sea. Now, it is channelled into the *levada* system, which are artificial channels.'

Katherine smiled her thanks. 'I suppose that's why you see so much cultivation as you look up to the mountains. All those small plots, all flourishing. It's a wonderful sight.'

'It is indeed,' the assistant agreed, and moved to serve another customer.

Katherine wandered from the shop and looked about her, feeling lost. For the first time she felt really alone. It had occurred to her to go to Horacio, but she could not forget the part he and Jorge had played in Luis's little subterfuge of recording that conversation.

A pang of hunger told her it was time she had her midday meal. Walking on, she found a café, eating as much as she could manage of the meal she had ordered, which was not a great deal despite its appetising flavour. Finishing with coffee, she paid her bill and wandered outside.

The guide book told her to take a bus or a taxi. The idea of using public transport in unknown territory worried her, so when a taxi drew alongside, asking if she would like to go anywhere, she got in eagerly.

The driver deposited her at the start of the walk, telling her it was really the wrong time of day—too hot, he said, better later—and she should have taken a sun-hat and should be wearing good shoes. As she paid him, he advised, 'Don't go too far, *senhora*. As soon as you are tired, turn back.'

Katherine stood still, taking in her surroundings. It was the first time she had been away from the immediate environs of the town, and was a little anxious. A group of boys played football, and when they saw her, stopped playing and surrounded her with interest. For a few moments she panicked, then smiled, and they grinned back.

At last she started walking, soon finding herself on the *levada* wall. There were babies splashing in plastic tubs, while their smiling, interested mothers and aunts and sisters embroidered nonstop, making exquisite tablecloths and blouses. There were vines growing and flowers were everywhere, blooming brilliantly from houses left and right.

The narrow wall beneath Katherine's feet was made of concrete and care was needed in where she placed her feet. All the time, the water flowed beside her. Flowers overhung the walk and Katherine pushed them aside in order to pass.

Now and then along the route she saw women kneeling down and scrubbing clothes. They were talking and laughing and seemed content. They smiled up at Katherine, greeting her in their own language, while she said, 'Hallo,' back.

There came into view, after some time, the magnificent sight of the Cabo Girão which, as Horacio had told her, was the world's second highest sea cliff. There were its terraced plots of land determinedly cultivated by the owners, or maybe the owners' tenants.

Walking on through a banana plantation, Katherine found that watching the two channels of the *levada* water running past was cooling. Oranges hung from branches overhead, spilling over back garden fences.

The way stretched ahead and Katherine was conscious of fatigue creeping up on her. Feeling the heat of the sun on her head, she stood still and shielded her eyes. If only she hadn't been growing so tired, nor the sun so hot on her uncovered head! If only she'd worn sensible shoes, as she had been warned! There was, she knew, no turning back. There was nothing she could do but go on.

She did not know how long she had been walking when she felt she could hardly take another step. Her sandal straps chafed her heels and toes. The top of her head burned more than ever. A drink, a few minutes' cover from the sun—any one of those things would have helped. With nowhere to sit, she crouched down and held her head, too exhausted to straighten.

There were footsteps approaching. They knew without doubt where they were going, but Katherine was so disorientated she could not judge the direction from which they came. She knew she should move to make way for the walker, since there was virtually no room for him to pass. Her efforts to rise were unsuccessful and she mumbled an apology.

Two gripping hands lifted her and she thought for a mad moment that she was about to be deposited in the *levada*. Beneath her body strong arms supported her weight with ease. The chest her head found itself against was as familiar to her sense of touch as the drumbeat of the heart was to her ears.

'You crazy, stupid little devil!' the voice snapped. 'I told you you were free to leave the island, not this world. Is that what you were trying to do? Get my sympathy?'

'Just taking a walk,' she told him in a small voice. 'I didn't know what else to do on my own.'

A few moments passed of unbelieving silence. 'Just taking a walk.' He uttered the words long-sufferingly. 'No head covering, no refreshment—and look at those ridiculous sandals! Did you think you were going for a stroll down an English country lane?'

Katherine lay supine in his arms.

'How did you get to the start of the walk?' Luis persisted. 'Taxi? Didn't the taxi driver warn you?' She nodded again. 'You ignored his warning?' He saw the guide book in her hand. 'And that booklet, which I'm sure gives instructions about suitable clothes?'

'I just thought I'd go a little way, but the view drove me on, and on ...'

'You're not safe to be let out on your own!'

Katherine was too tired to refute the dogmatic statement. He turned and walked back the way he had come. 'You can put me down,' she remarked. 'You might miss your footing——'

'I know these *levadas* like the back of my hand. I've walked the length of them, into the mountains. When I was a child I played along them.'

'Like the boys I saw back there?' He nodded.

After a while, he asked, 'Do you feel like walking now?'

'Yes,' she lied, dreading the rub of her sandal straps again but guessing he might be feeling the strain of her weight.

He slid her to the ground and led the way, walking confidently, oblivious to the view, which caught at Katherine's breath. The way he wore his well-cut but casual brown slacks, his checked leisure shirt made her heart miss a beat as she recalled that this was the way he had dressed in the first days of their marriage.

'They're wonderful,' Katherine called partly to attract Luis's attention, partly in true admiration, 'these *levadas*.' He stopped and gazed around, as if surprised by her comment.

'I've known them for so many years,' he explained, 'I see them as part of the scenery, but they're vital to the island's life.' He looked at the water flowing beside them, making its way downhill in a continuous stream.

'Those amazing terraces all over the mountains,' she commented, 'it gives the country a fantastic look, as though the hills and mountains were pleated!'

'Those plots of land wouldn't flourish without the water these channels carry. The clouds release their rain over the central mountains. It's said the island is a huge reservoir. If the water was not channelled, it would all pour back into the sea.'

They came at last to a small diversion where a road branched one way, a cobbled path the other. 'I'll show you an excellent view,' Luis stated, turning to Katherine. 'Are your sandals hurting?'

Her momentary hesitation before answering told him without words that they were. He tutted, then swung her again into his arms, looking down into her face which smiled happily back at him. 'If this foolishness is what happens when I let you out of "prison", then I'd better take you back to it again.'

'Oh,' she sighed, her head falling against his shoulder, 'yes, please!'

Luis stopped. 'So I'm your gaoler again? Is that what you want?'

Katherine nodded, then closed her eyes so that she wouldn't see his look of triumph. 'To live with you, just to live with you,' she confessed. Immediately she lifted her head and added mischievously, 'up here, sleeping rough in these wonderful mountains. You and me, man and woman, in a cave. No worries, no responsibilities, no wealth or riches to cause quarrels and unhappiness.'

He continued walking. 'No money to buy food, no way to keep clean, no place to sleep, no means of keeping out the cold. You'd soon scuttle back to civilisation.'

'What about you?' she flared. 'You wouldn't be able to stand it for long, you and your work, your craving for more and more money and power, your "spoiled rotten" way of life.'

'Thanks for the insults,' he responded equably, 'but I'll tell you one thing. I'd last out a damned sight longer than you. I'm tough, my girl, I can weather any storm, whether it's emotional or physical.'

'Tough guy, aren't you?' she taunted, running her

finger down his nose. 'What would you do if I left you, like my mother left my father?'

'Tear you to bits,' he said without emotion, making his statement all the more deadly.

'Then get right back to work?'

'Right back to work, kitten.' Despite the endearment, his tone had a cold sound. He set her on her feet. 'Look at that,' he said, and Katherine looked. 'It's the Socorridos River valley.'

As far as the eye could see, there were banana plantations. There again was the terraced landscape, descending in giant steps down the steeply sloping sides of the mountains. Beyond the immediate slopes there were yet more, and towering over the scene a mountain barrier rising high and, as the sun momentarily vanished, darkly menacing in the distance.

Even here there were houses, built on the lower slopes and straggling in a white and orange-coloured line down towards the valley. Katherine turned to Luis, eyes filled with wonder. 'It was worth every bit of that walk to see this,' she admitted. 'It's magnificent!' As she took a few steps forward, Luis's hand shot out.

'Don't go another step,' he warned. 'There's a hair-raising drop to the left of us on this path, with no protection whatever. And,' his arm went round her as he turned her back, 'whatever you might think of me, I don't want to lose you, *amada*.'

Smiling up at him, she answered, '*Muito obrigado, senhor!*'

His fist playfully bounced her chin. 'Impudent kitten,' he admonished with a smile, and they walked on. Soon afterwards, he told her, 'Here is where we leave the walk.' He led her down a steep slope to where he had parked his car. Adjusting the front passenger seat, he helped her into it, saying, 'Now lie back and relax.'

Murmuring her thanks, Katherine sought and used the

head-rest, closing her eyes. Her feet ached and her head felt heavy.

'Water?' Luis, beside her, offered her a bottle and her hands came out eagerly. 'No cup,' he said. 'You'll have to drink it from the bottle.'

'I'm not the fussy one,' she retorted, her look full of meaning. The water slid, wonderfully cool, down her parched throat.

He took the bottle from her and his smile taunted. 'I'm not fussy, either,' he asserted, and tipped back his head, taking huge gulps, wiping his mouth afterwards with the back of his hand. 'Like wine,' he commented, replacing the top. 'Reminds me of old times.'

His slanted, sideways glance challenged her to ask for an explanation. She did not take it up, despite the fact that she was itching to do so. It was good to see that glimpse of the Luis she had come to love so deeply before she knew his true position in life.

'Where now?' she asked.

He looked over her recumbent figure lazily. 'Shall I let my butterfly go again?' he reflected aloud. 'Shall I pick her from the net and throw her into the wind, letting it take her on the air currents and out of my sight for ever?'

Katherine was silent for a long time. The thought of the freedom which she knew he was genuinely offering her appalled her. Life away from him would be unliveable. She could not be like her mother and throw all this love away. But if he wanted her to go ...

'Are you saying you're tired of me already?' He did not answer. 'Because, you see,' her eyes turned to dwell on the blue of the sea, and away to the horizon, 'I'd like to stay.' There might have been a statue beside her for all the sound and movement he made. 'Just as long,' she added, 'as you call off the secret surveillance.'

'All surveillance cancelled,' Luis responded at last, 'as from now.'

The engine sound died away. They were in Luis's private parking place beside the hotel.

'Thank you for coming to find me.' Katherine's smile was warm as it was turned on her husband. 'I didn't realise——'

'There's a lot you don't realise,' he cut her off abruptly. 'Go and change, especially those things on your feet, put on a swimsuit and I'll take you to the Country Club. I'm a member. There's a pool, amongst many other amenities. We'll swim and sunbathe. It'll make a change from the hotel.'

'Are you sure——?'

'If you ask me if I can spare the time, *I will throttle you.*' He leaned across and opened her door. On the way back, his mouth found hers, his arms enfolded her, then she was free to move. 'Don't be long.'

Breathless, she nodded, running to do his bidding. I'm always doing what he tells me, she thought without anger, he's that kind of man. There's an invisible thread stretching between myself and him. I'd never be the one to break it, never. . . .

Luis parked the car in the forecourt of the Country Club, where the palm trees stretched high towards the blue skies. There was a tea-room with tables and chairs outside. Luis led Katherine across a lawn and down a flight of steps to the pool. It was surrounded by greenery, shrubs and plants and over it all, the tall palm trees.

The turquoise-coloured water looked immensely inviting. Luis found a place on the grass surround, pulling Katherine down beside him. He looked around and Katherine followed his gaze, seeing the visitors stretched out to soak up the sun, or running to the pool's side and jumping in with shouts of pleasure.

Beyond the immediate vicinity of the Country Club, there were apartment blocks, white buildings with balconies. There were houses, too, with the familiar orange-tiled roofs. As a daunting yet magnificent backcloth, the mountains, free of the cloud which sometimes veiled them, rose high to catch the sun or blend with the blue of the sky. Luis pointed out that through a gap between the apartment blocks it was possible to see a blue mist which was, he said, the sea. Blue and gold, Katherine thought, always I'll associate those colours with this wonderful island.

'I've brought towels,' she told him.

'There was no need. Down the steps over there are changing rooms where towels are provided. I should have told you not to bother. However, since you have,' he pulled off his shirt, 'it saves me a journey.'

A few moments later his slacks were put aside and his swimming trunks were a deep blue. He lay back, waiting for her to follow his example. Katherine saw the leanness of the man she loved and found her muscles tensing in her effort to stop herself from throwing herself on to him.

Luis saw her covert glance and smiled, closing his eyes. She could not prevent a sudden shyness manifesting itself as a deep pink in her cheeks. 'Are you,' she asked, to hide her embarrassment, 'a good swimmer?'

'Strange, isn't it,' he mused, 'how a woman who's my wife doesn't know whether or not I swim well. Yes, a very good swimmer.'

By now, Katherine had removed her skirt and sun-top and pushed them, with the matching jacket, into the large bag she had brought. The towels she extracted from it were embroidered with the name 'Hotel Sereno'.

Turning, she found his eyes on her. Their expression—of male admiration and 'wanting'—had her skin prickling and her heart beating as though it had a race to win.

Her eyes had the sparkle of the sea mixed with sun. 'Race you to the pool!' she challenged, and made for the water. Climbing backwards down the steps, she saw with disappointment that Luis was standing but had not followed. The impact of the cold water on her sun-warmed skin made her gasp. Holding on to the side, she trod water to acclimatise her body to the sudden temperature change.

When she saw Luis approaching, his long, strong legs making straight for her, fists belligerently on his lean hips, she pushed with her legs and swam across to the centre. The splash he made as he hit the water sent waves all around her. Others shouted and laughed at the impact, some speaking English, others Portuguese, yet others the many and varied European languages. He had caught her up and was in front of her. He seized her arms and floated face down, pulling her round to float beneath him. His kiss was brief but so searching she had to fight for breath. He did not let her go but made her swim with him, long pulling strokes that made her plead with him to carry on without her. He had proved beyond doubt that he was, as a swimmer, in a far higher category than she could ever aspire to. The coldness of the water struck her again and she shivered as she watched him pull away. Turning to swim on his back, he saw her arms wrapped around her body. 'Out,' he ordered at once, 'the pool's not heated.'

The warmth of the sun was bliss after the shivering attack, stilling her limbs and relaxing her. Lying back on the grass, she let her swimsuit dry on her. Luis returned, dripping, picking up a towel and rubbing his face and shoulders. Then he lay beside Katherine, but with his head turned towards her.

'I enjoyed the kiss,' he said lazily. 'We should do it more often.'

Her hand reached out to rest on the dark mat of hair on his chest. It was damp under her fingers. It stirred her desire just touching him. 'I love you,' she confided spontaneously, adding at once, in case she had given too much away, 'just as you are now, just you, minus the outward signs of your position and wealth.'

'You mean clothes? You want me to walk around like this all the time?' He was up on his elbow, laughing into her face, his white teeth flashing.

Katherine half rose in protest at his deliberate misunderstanding of her meaning, but he pushed her down and went with her. Once again his mouth captured hers, forcing her soft lips apart with his hard, insistent kisses. His hand rested, in indisputable ownership, on her breast. In immediate response her arms curved round his neck.

'Luis,' she spoke against his mouth, her eyes dazzled by the brilliance in his, 'if only we could forget the rest of the world! If only it could be just the two of us.'

'Come out of your dream, *querida*. Accept me as I am—not the pathetic failure of a man needing your financial support that you thought I was, but a successful businessman who——'

'Who's so rich you make my father look poor. And to think I ran away from him, and home, because he had so much money! Yet you're asking me to accept you as you are—almost a millionaire. I can't do it, Luis.' Then she reached up and pulled his head lower so that she could tease his mouth with kisses.

When they drew apart they were laughing, arms and bodies entwined. There was a shout of 'Luis!' He turned reluctantly, recognised the person calling and waved. There was a brief conversation in Portuguese. Luis glanced down at Katherine, then spoke to the man again, who had not moved closer.

Luis was shaking his head. '*Apresento-lhe a Senhora de Freitas, a minha mulher.*' He added, 'She is English.'

'Your wife?' the man asked, seeming astonished. 'But surely she is not the one——' He finished the sentence in Portuguese.

Luis, leaning back on his elbows, glanced again at

Katherine. He took up the man's own words. 'Yes, she is the one, João, the only one.'

Understanding seemed to come to the man and he nodded knowingly. 'Senhora de Freitas,' he called, 'I am very pleased to meet you.'

Katherine nodded and smiled. When he had gone, she frowned. 'Is he a friend of yours?' she asked Luis.

'A friend and colleague.'

'What did he mean when he said "surely she isn't the one"? Which "one"?'

'You heard my answer. I told him you were *the* one.' He spoke more distantly and Katherine thought it wise to say no more on the subject.

'Luis!' This time the voice was feminine, and husky too. It was disturbingly familiar to Katherine. *I know Luis, that voice had said, I know him well.*

Footsteps approached, the heels of sandals clicking on the pool surround. The owner of those sandals was very sure of herself indeed. Luis was getting to his feet. Katherine looked at the muscled strength of his legs and thighs, the lean body, the dark head held high. He's mine, she thought, no other woman's going to take him from me.

'Darling!' The huskiness wound round Luis's tanned body like the arms that crept to link behind his neck. 'You're a sly one, getting married and not telling me. How could you, knowing how much I——'

'Delphine,' Luis's sharp voice sliced off the last two emotive words, 'meet my wife, Katherine.' He released himself from the clinging arms and his hand caught Katherine's wrist as she rose and stood beside him.

Delphine's provocative mouth formed itself into a smile. 'We have met, have we not, Senhora de Freitas? In fact,' to Luis, 'I took your wife's parcel of handicrafts to your hotel this afternoon, only to be told that you were both out. You had gone, they said, to the Country Club. I left the parcel at reception and came here to find you.'

Luis turned to Katherine. 'What did you buy at Delphine's shop?'

Katherine shrugged, as if it were of no consequence. 'Mrs Evans has just told you—handicrafts, souvenirs— you know.'

Luis's eyebrows lifted. 'Why? Are you planning to leave, after all?' His voice had gone cold, like the water in the pool, and Katherine's skin prickled.

Delphine listened, her smile broadening, her eyes as watchful as a tigress about to make a killing. The woman's whole demeanour spurred Katherine to action. In a purely primitive response, she moved in front of Luis, putting her arms round his neck as Delphine had done. 'I'll never leave you. I love you far too much to let you go. You know that, darling, don't you?' Her cheek nestled against the very male chest, and her ear picked up the quickened throb of the heart of him.

Katherine expected to be put from him as he had dealt with Delphine, but he played up to her, tipping her chin and put darting kisses over her mouth. Only then did he straighten, indicating that she should loosen her hold.

In the end, Katherine thought, he had treated them both in the same way, a fact which Delphine did not miss. The smile, which had set into an unattractive line, relaxed into a playful pout. 'Katherine—if I may call you that?' Katherine nodded. Delphine continued, 'He treats all his women in the same way. They're there for his leisure time, which is little enough, heaven knows. But make no mistake, work, and only work, comes first in Luis de Freitas's life.'

There was no mistaking the bitterness in eyes and voice. Luis smiled, eyes flashing, black hair gleaming in the sun. Then his arm went round his wife's bare shoulders, but he spoke to the woman who faced him. 'I remain your friend, Delphine. Have I not helped you in the past?'

'And you'll continue to help me in the future, darling Luis?'

Katherine's limbs grew tense. They seemed to have forgotten her presence.

'Why should I not?' Luis answered.

Delphine's spiteful gaze rested on Katherine. 'Why not, indeed!' With a wave, she left them.

Watching her go, Katherine knew what the man called João had meant when he had asked, *But surely she is not the one—?*

Delphine Evans *was* 'the one', the other woman in her husband's life.

They had had long cold drinks in the club's teahouse. Now they sat in the car which was parked nearby. Katherine glanced at her husband, wanting to talk, but his brooding profile kept her silent.

What was he thinking about? she wondered. She wondered also at the fact that, although she was his wife, and close though they had been physically, she still felt shut out from his mind.

'My house,' he said at last, 'it's time I took you there.'

'It's my house, too, now, isn't it, Luis?' It was a sincere question, but his answering glance was cynical. 'Surely laying claim to something I've built with my "ill-gotten gains", as you would call it, is abhorrent to you?'

Her shoulders lifted and fell. 'Have your fun at the expense of my principles!' Katherine stared at the intense green of the shrubs, in the gardens of the club, at the stirring trees, the palms spreading their waving leaves. 'I should still like to see *your* house.'

'Good, because one day before long you'll be moving there. A hotel is not a place to make a home.'

'*I'll* be moving there. What about you?'

'Weekends, maybe. Whenever I can spare the time.'

They were out of the club grounds now and driving

through the outskirts of Funchal.

'How do you expect your house to be a home without you to share it with me?' she asked.

'I thought you wanted to be free.' His tone was bland.

'You mean *you* want to be free—of me, so that you can pursue your "friendship" with Delphine Evans.'

His profile had grown remote. 'Think what you like to think about that.'

I will, she thought, I will. The lump in her throat did not melt into tears, so her eyes were not blurred as she gazed at the beauty of the island as each new turn of a corner brought an even more impressive view. They were heading for the hills and mountains, climbing all the time, driving on roads which were well kept but narrow, round bends which had her holding back the gasps lest they distracted the driver.

Down there, as she gazed, the ocean broke constantly in a creaming froth at the foot of the cliffs, or round the rocks. Always there was that white edge to the sea, making a perfect foil to the many shades of blue both above and below. And over everything, the thriving, terraced plots of land; the banana plantations, the sugarcane and the vines, the benign and benevolent sun shone down.

Luis turned at last into a short driveway, braking in front of a modern house. Like the many others in the near distance, it perched on a hillside and basked in all the beauty it surveyed. The walls of the house were a striking blue-green, the shutters and window surrounds painted white.

There were two storeys above the ground floor. This, Luis explained, was where the housekeeper and her husband, Maria and José, lived. Above them were the living quarters, each with its own balcony, railed in by decorative ironwork. Flowers had been trained to grow across the roofs of the balconies. Across the first, vines grew, while over the second, pink-shaded bougainvillea spread itself with a striking grace into cupped or open flowers.

'It's beautiful, Luis. Shall we go inside?'

'So even you, despite your principles, can't wait to see the goodies my money has bought.'

She turned on him. 'Once you shared *my* home, poor as it was. I didn't make sarcastic comments about your principles, nor did I say unpleasant things to you for failing to run your father's business properly—which was what I was led to believe at the time.'

'Agreed. So we call a truce. Oh, and,' he pulled her towards him, 'welcome to my—now our—house.' His kiss was fleeting but potent. He left her wanting more.

It was as they walked inside that Katherine recalled that Aunt Olga lived there, too. The interior decoration, the furniture, the fittings were elegant but colourful, sometimes overpoweringly so. The quality, however, was good and it was plain that no expense had been spared.

'As you know,' Luis remarked dryly, 'my stepmother's taste sometimes borders on the gaudy.'

'Like her clothes,' Katherine agreed, and they smiled at each other. 'It looks as though you gave her a free hand where the decorations and everything else is concerned.'

'I'm not here all that often,' he told her offhandedly.

'You mean you live at the hotel most of the time?'

'My work is there.'

'And like my father, you just can't leave that.'

He glanced at her at the sound of bitterness, but did not respond. Katherine wandered to one of the windows of the main living area. 'The view—it's breathtaking,' she commented, unable to tear her eyes from the steeply sloping land, the cliffs dropping down to the restless ocean.

'The mountains can be seen from the back. Come upstairs to see the bedrooms.'

Only in the main bedroom did it seem that Luis had had his way. The furniture was modern but unpretentious.

Again the quality was good, the colours being muted and attractive.

'I like your taste,' Katherine commented, turning to him. He bowed mockingly. 'But I couldn't live here, Luis. I'd feel totally out of place. There's—well, so much of Aunt Olga about it. Not just that.' She stared out of the window and noted the balcony outside where bougainvillea flowed in a waterfall of brilliant colour from the balcony roof.

'Don't tell me.' His voice was hard. 'Your damned principles!'

Better, she thought, to let him believe that than tell him the truth—that living there without him, magnificent though the scenery and the house itself were, could scarcely be called living at all.

She wandered out and into the bedrooms at the rear of the house. As he had said, the mountains rose to the heights with houses clinging to the steepness, then fell to deep ravines and valleys, taking the persistent white and orange-roofed dwellings with them.

'Is this a guestroom?' Katherine asked, glancing round, noting the adjoining bathroom, the comfortable chair, the writing desk. Here the shades were less intense, therefore far more tolerable. 'Where's Aunt Olga's room?'

'Along the corridor. Would you like to see it?'

Katherine screwed up her eyes, laughing. 'No, thanks— I can imagine. That's sufficient!'

Luis laughed with her, and again she wanted to throw her arms about him and ask him to love her, then love her again, and she would believe they were back in that old bed of hers where they had rolled to the centre ... Her eyes opened to the polished, expensive reality around her, then lifted in half-disguised anguish to his.

'What are you thinking?' he asked softly.

Katherine turned round to the view again. 'I won't tell you.' She paused. 'I can't tell you.'

'I can imagine, too.' He came behind her, linking his hands round her waist and pulled her close to him. 'It's no good, kitten. You took me in marriage. This is my kind of life. You're my wife.' His hands moved upwards to hold her breasts. 'I shall never let you go.' His whisper kissed her ear and a shiver sent pinpricks of pleasure through her body.

He turned her, cradled her, bent her backwards and his mouth came down to probe and explore the sweet offerings of hers. Her fingers clawed at his shirt and clung and she was wandering in a dawn haze of happiness. At last he straightened her. 'You're mine,' he affirmed, 'mine. Do you hear? If you ever look at another man, I'll——' His gaze turned piercing and she grew strangely afraid. 'I'll make you pay for it for the rest of your life!'

CHAPTER NINE

The parcel of souvenirs and handicrafts which Delphine had delivered from her shop were placed on a coffee table in the sitting room. Katherine decided to defer unpacking them until another time and put the parcel in a cupboard.

She dressed for dinner while Luis showered and changed into his evening clothes.

He still used the smaller bedroom, which troubled Katherine. To her, a true marriage meant a sharing of everything, not only a bed.

As she stood in bra and waist slip, inspecting the row of evening gowns he had bought her, a vision of Delphine Evans' personality came to her. Shallow, sophisticated, glossy ... Glossy! Her hand moved to choose a dress—and her arms were captured by hands which turned her.

'The sun is giving you a golden-girl look,' Luis remarked, his eyes sleepy. 'Look at you—a married woman but with the freshness of an untouched girl.'

'Does that displease you?' she replied, with a provocative glance through her lashes. 'Do you prefer, say, the more mature woman, married before maybe, with a husky voice, who winds herself round you, calls you "darling"....'

He stopped her deliberate needling with the ruthless pressure of his mouth, pulling her to him, running his hands down her arms and up again over her shoulders. He slipped down the straps, fondled the filling shape of her, kissed potent places into anticipatory hardness.

She laughed with pleasure as his lips brought a shivering warmth to her throat which spread down to titillate her nerve endings. As his hands moulded and his fingers caressed, she felt herself drawn increasingly into the circle of his desire.

'Later,' she protested, against his mouth, 'later, darling. Let me dress.'

'I'd prefer it if you didn't,' he murmured, his hands on her hips, his eyes on the swell of her breasts. Reluctantly he released her. 'If there weren't a few letters for me to sign, I'd follow my desires here and now.'

Katherine frowned. 'Letters to sign?' She adjusted the straps he had lowered and pushed back her tousled hair. 'Does work follow you everywhere?'

'If you pout your lips at me, senhora,' he drawled, 'I will punish them with mine for their audacity.'

Her hand lifted to cover her mouth. He laughed, straightened his jacket and went to the door leading into the sitting-room. 'I shall come for you in fifteen minutes. We're going out after dinner. There's a restaurant which turns itself into a kind of night club. Tonight, a group of Madeiran folk dancers will be there. Make yourself look even more beautiful, my love—if that is possible.'

When he returned she was dressed and waiting. The vision she had had of Delphine would not go from her mind, so she had, she hoped, by her choice of dress, superimposed herself upon the image Luis seemed to have in his mind of Delphine.

Whether his reaction had anything to do with the woman who had just stopped short of telling him in front of his wife, that she loved him, Katherine could not tell. He stood in the doorway, silent and unreadable, as his eyes wandered over her. The dress was of cherry red satin, the material glowing softly in the lights around the room. The sleeves were wrist-length, an opening from the low shoulderline downwards only partly closed with lacing.

The neck was low both back and front, the top also laced, revealing tantalising glimpses of white skin swelling from the cleft between her breasts. The top, the skirt, fitted perfectly and showed the shape of her to full advantage.

'Will I do?' Katherine asked, trying for some kind of response, whether it was praise or not. 'You bought it for me,' she added, his continued silence putting her on the defensive. 'Don't blame me if——'

'The only thing I blame you for,' he said at last, 'is for looking so damned beautiful you make me want to ravish you right now.'

'You said we were going out,' she declared, hoping he would accept her scheme to divert him from the blatant invitation which the dress seemed to be offering him.

He smiled dryly, showing he had observed her tactics. Then he held out his hand, and she put hers into it. 'Come, we'll go down to the grillroom. That's the only way I'll be able to keep my hands off you!'

He led her up the spiral staircase, alongside which there ran a continuous wall of glass. Katherine paused, first to look down at the illuminated pool, then lifting her eyes to see one of the most beautiful sunsets she had ever seen.

It was sinking below one of the mountains and its golden rays touched a nearby peak, creating an illusion of the reflected beams being flung in all directions. As if echoing the thought, there came a distant shower of fireworks in the evening sky. In the main streets of the town neon lighting came and went, advertising Madeiran wines, hotels or discotheques.

Doors leading to the grillroom were opened by smiling men, and, with Luis walking tall and handsome at her side, Katherine stepped forward into the semi-darkness. Candles flickered on circular tables, lighting was recessed and discreet. The carpet underfoot was thick-piled and luxurious.

Luis spoke in Portuguese to the head waiter and they were escorted to a table half in light, half in darkness, the

extra illumination coming from an area in the centre
which appeared to be reserved for dancing.

As they settled themselves and the head waiter hovered
while they selected their dishes, Katherine asked, 'Is there
a cabaret in here in the evenings?'

Luis nodded, adding, 'It starts late and ends late. Too
late for young women who need their—sleep.'

Katherine's eyes threw back the reply she could not,
because of the head waiter's presence, put into words.
Luis smiled, asked for her order then, with her permission
chose for them both.

As they drank the dry, amber-coloured wine called,
Luis informed her, *verdelho*, and which he had chosen as
an aperitif, he told Katherine about the vineyards he
owned. 'The harvest,' he told her, 'takes place between
August and October. It's a happy occasion. You must
come with me when it happens and I'll explain the different processes to you.'

'You think I'll still be here then?' she queried, her smile
as innocent of guile as she could make it.

'You'll leave this island without me at your peril,' was
his unequivocal, and entirely serious, answer.

He chose another kind of wine for their main course
and yet another, of which Katherine had only a small
quantity, with their desserts. It was, he said, called *boal*
and its semi-sweet taste, coming after the other wines, was
just a little too much for her to take.

'I'll be too drunk to enjoy the evening in front of us,'
she laughed, seeing him in a strange haze in which he was
there opposite her, but somehow faded and was lost, only to
emerge again. She did not know whether it was the wine
or a curious trick of her unconscious mind which was caus-
ing the illusion, but whatever the cause, she did not like it.

'Tomorrow,' he told her casually, reappearing after
having faded, 'I shall be going to Lisbon. I'll be away for
about a week.'

If the chair had come to life and thrown her to the floor she could not have been more shocked. After taking a long drink of the dark coffee from the cup in front of her, she asked, 'Could I come with you? I've never been to Portugal.'

Even as she asked, she knew his answer, she could tell from the closed look on his face. 'I may be going with Delphine. She has business in Lisbon, too, in connection with her craft shop. She's considering opening another store there.'

Katherine's hand was shaking as she replaced the cup. 'You're going with Mrs Evans. I should have known!'

Luis reached across and took her hand, gripping it. 'Stop——'

There was a discreet cough beside them.

'Senhor de Freitas,' the head waiter interrupted, 'you are required on the telephone. In your office, senhor.'

Luis nodded, dropped Katherine's hand and with an 'Excuse me' so polite she might have been a stranger, he strode away.

In the five minutes in which he was absent, Katherine clenched her hands in her lap. Over and over again she said to herself, I asked him to marry me, I asked him to marry me. I can't complain now if his former girl-friend beckons and he goes running.

'It was Delphine,' Luis informed her, sitting down. 'She has confirmed that she's joining me on the journey.'

Katherine wanted to say, It doesn't matter if she is, I could still go with you. His refusal, which she knew he would give, would be too humiliating to bear. What was it Horacio had said the day he had met them at the airport?

'Ah, those "other women" which these young brides hate so much!'

Horacio was right, Katherine thought bitterly. 'I suppose,' she said, 'this grillroom is where you brought

Delphine Evans to dine before you met me? You said you'd "wined and dined" here before.'

'Naturally I had,' he answered tersely. 'I live here most of my time. But it's true,' his eyes flicked up lazily then down again, 'I have brought Delphine here.'

With an angry movement Katherine pushed back her chair, but the head waiter, always attentive, was there to help her. She walked from the grillroom, with Luis striding beside her. Luis wining and dining Delphine Evans, Luis making love to Delphine Evans. . . .

At that moment, with the other guests watching, the men openly admiring herself, the women more secretly admiring Luis, he seemed more out of her reach than ever.

Luis helped Katherine into the front seat of the car, adjusting the sparkle-scattered shawl which had slipped from her shoulders. She did not acknowledge the gesture with a smile, since her mind was still reeling over the fact that he was going away. He had given her scarcely any warning. Nor had he invited her to go with him. Instead he was taking another woman!

As Luis reversed to join the busy main road, Katherine made a conscious effort to divert her mind from her problems. The mountains, covered in starlike, twinkling lights, she found enchanting, brightening her mind as they did her vision.

They drove through Funchal, passing a large fountain, each individual spray of water being lit from underneath. The picture was of a flowing stream of gold.

The car climbed the mountain road while Katherine gazed with wonder at the glittering land reaching down to the sea. The moon was full and its light added a silver sheen to the thriving, terraced land. The car climbed resolutely against the gradient which the darkness seemed to make even steeper.

'What happens,' Katherine asked, to break the silence, 'if the brakes were to fail?'

'They won't. You can have every confidence in the car——' there was a significant pause, 'and in me.'

'I have, Luis,' was her whispered answer, implying so much more than the actual words conveyed.

Silence greeted the statement and Katherine told herself it was because he was concentrating so hard on his driving. The journey ended at last and the car was parked with many others a short distance from the restaurant.

'It's an eating place by day,' Luis explained as they made for the entrance, 'but in the evening it becomes a mountainside night club.' There were flowers in every corner of the entrance lobby. Smiling people greeted the newcomers, motioning them into the large darkened room where tables surrounded a dance floor.

Luis was recognised and welcomed with pleasure and esteem, attitudes to which Katherine was growing accustomed. On the table they occupied was a bottle of red wine, with glasses. There was a plate of small savouries and another bearing sweets.

A passing waiter was called by Luis, who spoke to him in his own language. The waiter nodded and removed the bottle of wine, returning almost at once with another bottle. He showed it to Luis, who nodded, tasted a sample, considered then nodded again. Smiling, the waiter poured the wine into Katherine's glass, then into Luis's.

When the waiter had left them, he raised his glass, inviting Katherine to join him. As their glasses touched, he said, enigmatically, 'To us and to the next generation.'

Katherine's glass halted on its way to her lips. 'What next generation?'

'Ours, *amada*, yours and mine. Who else's offspring but yours would I choose to father?' He laughed at her embarrassment. 'My love,' his hand covered hers, carrying it to his lips, 'you're very beautiful.'

'You told me that when we first met.'

'A typically English way to accept a compliment! Then, you were a lovely girl. Now you are an enchantingly attractive woman.'

The lowered lighting, the scent of the flowers scattered around, the wine she had already imbibed, were having an effect on her reflexes. 'I'll drink to your toast, Luis darling,' she told him with sparkling eyes. 'To the children we will have one day—and may they never know the worry and the heavy weight of responsibility that money and its constant pursuit brings.'

His eyes hardened, his jaw thrust forward. 'To our children,' he said tersely, and drank.

Katherine savoured the sweet, full-bodied taste of the wine, inhaling its heady aroma. 'Mm, it's beautiful,' she commented, holding it to a nearby light and studying its clear topaz colour. 'What is it called?'

'Malvasia, better known as Malmsey wine, made famous way back in the fifteenth century when the Duke of Clarence was reputed to have drowned himself in a butt of it.'

Katherine nodded. 'It's a well-known tale.'

'As my uncle Horacio once said, what a wonderful way to go!'

Katherine laughed and sipped some more, feeling the warmth of the wine spread through her, adding itself to the wines she had drunk over dinner. 'I swear I couldn't walk straight if I tried,' she exclaimed.

'Why worry, with me to support you?' The narrow-eyed gleam betrayed the double meaning, but her mood was too mellow to rise to his taunt.

The sound of talking increased as the number of guests grew. A small band played music for dancing, but only a handful of couples rose. The lighting was dimmed and the moonlight, shining on the trees outside, shed its silvered beams on to the darkened room.

The romantic atmosphere lowered barriers and Katherine's hand stretched across the table. 'Luis?' Smiling faintly, Luis placed hers in his upturned palm. 'I'll miss you,' she confided.

'You will?' The romance had not got to him as it had to Katherine, newcomer and dazzled tourist, or so she regarded herself. It had rolled off him like raindrops from a waterproof coat. 'You surprise me. If you run true to family form, you won't be here when I return.'

She snatched her hand away, but her retort was cut off by a change in the atmosphere. The lights came on and a group of local folk dancers entered, striking in their scarlet and white costumes. The girls wore striped, multi-coloured skirts, red swirling capes over white blouses and laced waistcoats. Their partners, dark-haired young men, looked handsome in white suits and wearing scarlet sashes around their waists.

The music for their dancing came from a team of similarly dressed men. When the display of folk dancing was over, the dancers broke off and walked into the audience, each of the group taking someone by the arm and leading them on to the dance floor.

One of the young men dancers approached and took Katherine's hand. With a defiant glance at Luis, she followed the young man to the dancing area. No one had approached Luis, she noticed, although there were many other men guests who had been selected by the young women.

The dancers and the partners of their choice formed a great circle which folded in on itself two or three times. It was when they were still and waiting at last, many of the tourists looking about them smiling but apprehensive, that a voice said, 'Why, Katherine, hi!'

'Dan! I'm so pleased to see you. What do I have to do?'

'Exactly what everyone else does. I didn't know you

were here. Is my mighty employer here with you?'

'My husband? Of course. I didn't see you, either.'

'It's the lighting, low and romantic, or so they say. I came with a group of tourists. I act as a courier in between my painting sessions. The hotel lays on coach trips, and I go with them to explain the scenery. You're good scenery, Katherine. You look great.' The circle began to move. 'See you again, maybe.'

Dancing began, the folk dancers and the newcomers mixing and holding hands, the great circle moving slowly. A member of the dancing team then broke away, choosing a partner of the opposite sex. Katherine was chosen almost at once by a smiling, white-suited young man. Together with the other chosen partners, she squatted on the floor with the dancers, clapping hands with them in a certain sequence.

When this was over, a ring was formed again and each dancer produced a scarf and again chose a partner of the opposite sex. Once again Katherine was selected. The young man placed the scarf round her neck and led her with it to the centre. Removing the scarf, he placed it on the floor between them. He knelt down, pulling her to join him, then he kissed her on both cheeks.

He handed the scarf to her and indicated that she should choose a man from the circle and repeat the process. Which man? she thought. Dan? Dare I—? Why not? she asked herself defiantly. Luis was going away with his girl-friend. Why should she not choose Dan, full of fun and laughter, and a clever artist, too?

Her eyes stopped short at Dan and he smiled as she approached. It grew into a grin as she put the scarf around his neck and pulled him to the middle of the circle. The scarf was then placed on the ground and they knelt and kissed—but it was not a chaste kiss on the cheek that she gave him. She made straight for his lips, putting her arms on his shoulders.

In the lowered lighting, his face grew scarlet. 'Hey,' he whispered, 'you'll get me fired for this!'

'Over my dead body,' she muttered back.

'Thanks a lot,' he answered, squeezing her arm as he accepted the scarf. To the clapping of the crowd, Katherine returned to the circle of people. When the game was over, guests and dancers joined hands again and a curving, snakelike line was formed. It wove between tables against the background of music played by the dancers' musicians.

They had not gone far when Katherine realised that the man immediately in front of her was Dan Stewart. 'Hi, again,' he said over his shoulder, and they exchanged smiles just as the weaving line was passing the table which Luis occupied.

His brooding look rested on Katherine's flushed face and she tossed her head defiantly at him. At that moment she did not care what he was thinking, but she knew it was the effect of the potent wines she had drunk in the course of the evening which had given her the courage to seem unmoved by his marked disapproval. Later, when the effect of the wine had disappeared, what of her false courage then?

Now they were in the sitting-room of their suite. Luis had a glass in his hand. Katherine played with the drawstring threaded through her low neckline. There was a scarlet flower in her hair placed there by Dan and which he had taken from a table display as he was escorting her back to Luis.

'Stop looking at me as if I'd just crawled from the gutter!' Katherine exclaimed, unable to stand the charged silence. 'I enjoyed the evening, every minute of it.'

'Especially holding Dan Stewart's hand, not to mention kissing him—not on the cheeks which is a rule of the game, but on the lips.'

'So I kissed another man! What's that to your taking your lover on a *business* trip?' She smeared the word with meaning, but had not bargained for the effect which her innuendo had on him.

He put down his half-finished drink and confronted her. He reached out and took the flower from her hair, throwing it down and grinding it under his heel.

'Why did you do that?' she cried. 'I was going to put it in water, then dry it and press it as a memento of—' Of my few happy weeks on this lovely island called Madeira, she had been going to say.

'Of a token of Dan Stewart's loving devotion,' Luis cut in, seizing her shoulders.

The look in his eyes frightened her. She twisted away and ran into the bedroom, then cursed herself for her stupidity. In this room she was trapped. There was no way out.

He was there again, in front of her. His eyes flared, his whole body emitted a blazing anger. 'I warned you,' he said harshly, 'that if you ever looked at another man, I'd make you pay. So pay you will!'

He jerked at the neckline of her dress. With both hands she gripped his wrist. 'Don't tear it, *please*! It's a beautiful gown and you——' Bought it for me, she thought but never said. Her fingers were clumsy as she sought for the drawstring, and he found it first, jerking and loosening it, easing the neck wider and wider. It was pulled down over her shoulders and arms, then it lay on the floor.

He swept her up and carried her to the bed, dropping her. His jacket and tie were flung away, his belt loosened. Moments later he was stretched beside her and then he disposed of the flimsy garments which covered her body. His mouth closed on hers, and it was as if gentleness and the tender touch were as unknown to him as to caveman himself.

His lovemaking was remorseless, drawing answering actions from her, arousing within her such primitive responses that her twentieth-century mind was lost in the cavewoman she had become under his harsh and brutal teaching. All barriers were torn away by his unsparing treatment of her, by the roughness of his lips and hands on her throat, her breasts, her thighs. He brought to her an ecstasy and rapture she had never dreamt of experiencing.

When his fury of lovemaking had abated and they lay satiated, side by side, tears sprang and rolled down to the pillow that cushioned her dazed head. Her body was on fire, but when the burning died away, she felt like a land devastated by a hurricane. How long, she wondered, would it take for her feelings to be restored to normality and for her to re-establish her self-respect? She had given herself in selfless love; Luis had taken her in total anger.

Now the covers were over them. He had turned away on to his side. Katherine swallowed the sadness and tried to remember the joy. But loving without love was like a sunset without the sun—colourless, meaningless and heralding a dark long night.

In the morning, he had gone. She had slept later than usual and the breakfast at the bedside had grown cold. In any case, she was not hungry. Her whole body ached with Luis's bruises, her mouth with his draining, punishing kisses.

It was as though some harboured resentment had been stored in him. The incident with Dan at the mountainside restaurant had plainly been the match to the fuse, the lovemaking the inevitable and devastating eruption.

Arousing herself, Katherine sat up, pulling the covers to her chin. He thought she would be gone by the time he had returned, did he? Well, she would be here. She would not give him on a plate, nor a silver salver, to her rival, however attractive and alluring that rival might be.

After showering and dressing, she went down to the foyer. Dan was in his seat and there was a stack of finished paintings beside him waiting to be collected. He called to her, 'Your portrait, Katherine—it's finished.'

Taking it from him, she studied it. 'It's good, Dan, too good. It makes me look beautiful.'

'Which you are.' He inspected her closely. 'You're radiant this morning.'

Colouring faintly, she shook her head. Dan's eyebrows were lifted in question, but she did not answer him. 'Luis has gone to Lisbon,' she told him.

'So you're off the leash today.'

'A week. And I'm free to do just as I like.'

Dan shook his head. 'I've noticed. Your husband hardly lets you out of his sight—if not his, then someone else's. So, what's to do? You're at a loose end? Come with us this morning. I'm the courier on an all-day coach tour into the mountains. There'll be a seat for you. Okay?'

'Okay, Dan. What time? Ten-thirty? I'll get ready. Oh, and thanks a lot for this. It's fine. How much?'

'For you, *senhora*,' he grinned, 'nothing. No, I mean it. Hang it in your room, or suite, or whatever. It'll make your husband admire you even more than he does now.'

'Don't be funny, Dan.' Her face clouded. 'I'm just another woman——' She stopped hurriedly. 'Forget that, will you?'

'Trouble? You surprise me. On the other hand,' he rubbed his head, 'I guess he could be a difficult customer when he likes. Good to his employees, but overstep the line and——' He pulled a straight hand across his throat.

Katherine smiled. 'See you in fifteen minutes. Round in the car park?' A customer was approaching Dan. Katherine lifted a hand and returned to the suite with her portrait.

The telephone rang as she arrived. Luis? she wondered,

and ran to answer. It was Horacio, and her heart fell a little—but not far, because Horacio's persistent optimism about life in general was infectious and uplifting.

'You are a temporary widow, I think, Katherine? Yes, I know Luis had gone away for a few days. He told me.'

Katherine responded in a falsely ingenuous tone, 'He didn't instruct you to keep an eye on me, did he?'

Horacio's hearty laughter brought a smile to her face. 'No one *instructs* me, Horacio de Freitas, not even my sometimes arrogant nephew. But no, he did not, except for saying I must make sure that everything you want is provided for you.'

'Everything is perfect, Horacio, thank you. Too perfect,' she added, without knowing why.

'How too perfect, Katherine?' Horacio seemed puzzled. Oh, yes, I remember—your principles, those strange principles. Some ideas you have inherited from your mother, are they not?'

'You can't inherit ideas, Horacio,' she responded, smiling.

'Can you not? Me, a simple, life-loving man, I would not know.'

'You're laughing at me, Horacio—I can hear.'

There was a burst of laughter. 'Well,' Horacio replied at last, 'if ever you are lonely, just come here to my office and Jorge and I, we will provide you with good company—including a discussion of those very strict principles of yours.'

'I'll come,' Katherine promised, and Horacio rang off.

A small crowd had gathered beside the coach which was to take the hotel guests on the tour. Painted along the side of the coach were the words, Horacio de Freitas Coaches, which meant, Katherine realised, that Horacio ran a tours business also.

Dan approached breezily, lifting his hand and saying, 'Hi.' He stood beside Katherine and when the others had climbed into the coach, he told her to take the front seat across from the driver. 'You'll be next to me,' he said. 'I say my piece through the microphone. The coach is air-conditioned and very comfortable—all of which is what you'd expect from your husband's uncle.'

Katherine smiled back at Dan's crooked smile. 'They're a very efficient family,' she commented, and followed the other passengers, seating herself where Dan had instructed.

The driver came along and Katherine recognised him faintly. He had been behind a desk in Horacio's main office the day she had visited the place. On seeing her, he gave a special nod. It seemed the recognition was mutual.

Dan spoke to him, using English, and the driver replied in the same language. Katherine studied the leaflet which she had found on the seat. It gave a map of the island, with their route picked out in red.

After a waiting period of five minutes for possible late-comers the driver started the engine and swung from the parking place into the road. Dan rose and, speaking through the microphone whose sound was relayed by inset roof speakers to the back of the coach, he asked for a show of hands from those whose language was not English. There was no response.

'That means,' Dan said, 'that you'll all understand me when I say good morning. My name is Dan. Our driver's name is Alberto. He's a fine driver. He knows all the bends in the road like the back of his hand. The brakes are fine and no one need be afraid of the steep drops you might see as we go along. If you are, just look away. Okay?'

There were a few answers of 'yes, thanks' and Dan resumed his seat. He smiled at Katherine, but did not speak. The coach made its way through Funchal, along the coast road and passing Câmara de Lobos, where Dan mentioned the visit of Sir Winston Churchill. The route

took them on and Katherine noticed that even the land
bordering on the sheer drops was cultivated into some
form of terraced fields.

Dan stood up to comment on them, adding that he
never ceased to marvel at the way the Madeirans put
every available piece of land to use. Katherine wondered
how anyone ever managed to tend them, speaking about
this to Dan.

'To be certain you've got a safe footing on that steep
ground,' she remarked, 'especially where the field ends
and the wall drops vertically to the next patchwork of
crops, you'd have to be born to it.'

Alberto, the driver, spoke and Dan heard what he had
said, conveying the message to Katherine. 'They are born
to it,' he told her, smiling, 'Alberto knows that from experience. When he was young, he helped his father, as
most children here do.'

Dan pointed, indicating a banana plantation, the fruit
hanging in small green bunches from the plants. He spoke
about this, adding that the bunch is ready for picking
when a small red flower appears at the bottom of the
bunch. He added, 'I'm told it takes twelve months for the
bananas to ripen.'

They passed through a number of small villages, and at
last they reached the first viewpoint of the tour called, as
Dan explained, Cabo Girão. Making their way through
the stalls and displays of the souvenir sellers, the group
followed Dan to the railings.

Here Katherine found that the view was magnificent.
The drop, Dan explained, was over one thousand, nine
hundred feet straight to the Atlantic. Agapanthus clung
to the top of the cliff, while pine, Dan pointed out, and
eucalyptus grew to the very edge.

Hundreds of feet below, Katherine noted with astonishment, farmers had cultivated even tiny plots of land,
terracing them and tending them until they flourished.

All the time, there was the swish of the waves foaming white against the base of the cliffs, curving round and away.

The tour continued, the terrain becoming wilder, but the cultivation of the land went intrepidly on. The number of houses built on the steep mountainsides had dwindled, painted white as were most of the others on the island, their roofs orange or red.

A stop was made for lunch in a village which was surrounded by high mountains. Dan joined Katherine at the table she had chosen, which looked out on the cobbled street and the steep green mountainside which rose on the other side of a stream which followed the line of the village street.

Mineral water was provided and the appetiser was a salad, followed by a fish or meat course. A bowlful of fresh strawberries finished the meal. For most of the time, the coach driver had helped behind the bar. Dan suggested that the café owners might be his friends or even relatives.

The tour continued, passing the rugged scenery, the passengers hardening themselves to the steep drops away from the twisting roads. As they stopped at another viewpoint, Katherine stared in wonderment yet again at the steep cliffs falling away to the ocean.

Blue and purple hydrangeas decorated the roadside and grass verges. Dan, beside her again, told her that the workmen, while repairing the road surfaces, planted the hydrangeas. 'It seems it helps with the road drainage,' he added.

The tour went on, as did the magnificent scenery. There was a stop for tea and as the coach party waited to be served, other customers started to sing. There was a small boy amongst the group at a large table and it appeared to be his birthday celebration.

The song was 'Happy Birthday', which the family sang

in Portuguese, while the members of the coach party, including Katherine and Dan, joined in in English. Everyone in the tea-room clapped and the small boy blushed fiercely.

At the end of the tour, Katherine alighted first, experiencing an unexpected sense of pride at the sight of the great white building that was the Hotel Sereno. She stood waiting as Dan helped the passengers down the steps of the coach. Some of them pressed coins and notes into his hand and he thanked them with a sincere smile. When the last person had gone, he counted the money which had been given to them, then handed it all over to the driver.

'Your need is greater than mine,' Katherine heard him say. 'I get paid well for my work, and anyhow I've got a fine home back in the States.'

Alberto, the driver, was delighted at Dan's generous gesture and drove away with a wave. Katherine looked at Dan with an admiring smile. 'That was kind of you,' she said, and he put his arm round her shoulders.

'I admire the Madeirans,' he confessed as they walked together towards the hotel entrance. 'They work hard. They don't sit back and wait for others to come along and help them, they get on with their lives, make the best of what they've got.'

Katherine nodded. 'You can see it all round you, like those magnificent mountains, covered in a patchwork of fields.'

The doorman bowed politely as Katherine entered. She was making for the lift when Dan called to her, 'Hey there, Katherine, you dining in your suite tonight?'

'Hadn't thought about it. Why?'

'Eat with me, in the restaurant overlooking the pool?'

'Why not? Just for you, I'll wear my mink and diamonds!'

'That dress you had on last night would do. I sure

loved you in that.' He was grinning, but Katherine frowned. The dress brought back memories she would rather forget.

'Not that one.'

Dan shrugged. 'Okay, okay, wear your bikini as far as I'm concerned.'

Their laughter echoed across the reception area and as Katherine turned to go, she noticed the doorman staring and the young woman at reception frowning.

In the suite she drooped. The events of the day had put to the back of her mind the deep unhappiness which, on waking that morning, had threated to swamp her. Now, all too vividly she recalled the tempestuous night she had spent with Luis—worse, the humiliation she had felt when, afterwards, instead of holding her lovingly in his arms, he had turned his back on her. Tonight would it be Delphine with whom he shared the long dark hours?

There was nearly an hour to be filled before dinner was served. She wandered through into the bedroom, opened the door of the cubboard in which Delphine's parcel had been placed, bent down to open it, but changed her mind. They were souvenirs, bought to be taken home as gifts. They had been purchased even before she knew of Delphine's existence. Had some kind of premonition prompted her to buy them?

CHAPTER TEN

HORACIO welcomed Katherine into his shop next morning as if he had not seen her for years.

'I said I would come,' she told him, smiling. Looking round, she saw Jorge who was looking at her somewhat doubtfully. She wanted to ask him what was wrong, but the other men were at their desks, or entering and leaving all the time.

'You have been lonely, eh?' Horacio asked. 'You are missing your loving husband?'

Katherine frowned, running a finger along the wood grain of his desk. 'I've been lonely, yes. But,' she forced herself to brighten, 'not alone.'

'Ah!' Horacio's finger lifted as if in admonition. 'I have been hearing.'

'Someone's been telling tales?' Katherine said sharply.

'Why?' Horacio's expressive face was innocent now. 'Are there "tales" to tell? You have not been able to wait only a few days for your husband's return?'

'What do you think I am, Horacio? A—a———'

'Don't say it, my child. Come.' He indicated his private office.

'Katherine?' She turned as Jorge called her. 'It is not right, Katherine. Not you, Luis's wife.'

Katherine frowned. 'What isn't right?'

'Senhor Stewart, he is nice, but here, it is not right.'

Katherine shook her head vigorously, then followed Horacio. 'A chair,' he offered, and sat down behind his desk.

'I don't know what Jorge was talking about,' she declared, with anger. 'What did I do but go on a coach tour yesterday with Dan as the guide, dine with him last night——' Horacio looked at her steadily. 'You must believe me,' she insisted. 'You don't surely think——'

'You are English, child. You do not know the ways of my countrymen, nor their standards.'

Her cheeks grew hot. 'I think you're insulting me, Horacio, and I don't like it.'

He leaned back, clasping his hands across his ample form. 'Good. I am glad you accuse me of insulting you, because it means there are no grounds for the unhappy thoughts I have been thinking.'

'None at all, Horacio. I've been friendly with Dan Stewart, just friendly. You do understand?'

'I understand, my dear. The only person you now have to convince is your husband.'

Katherine paled. His words came back, hitting her like a well-aimed blow. *If you ever so much as look at another man, I'll make you pay for the rest of your life.*

Horacio saw her distress. 'He will get to know, Katherine. He will ask questions, he will add up the answers.'

'And, like you, come to a false conclusion.'

'I will tell him the truth, you can trust me. Your principles—I would like to talk about them, but not here, Katherine. We will go to another place. Come, I will tell Jorge to take over. One day he will do that completely, when I grow old.'

Horacio took her in one of his taxis, through the busy streets of Funchal, past the lady flower sellers in colourful dress, surrounded by their beautiful blooms; past the jacaranda trees along the Avenida Arriaga.

The gradient steepened as they left Funchal behind. 'Where are we going?' Katherine asked at last.

'To Luis's house in the hills,' Horacio answered, preoccupied with driving.

Looking at the mass of bougainvillea pouring its bright

colour across the higher of the two balconies brought back poignant memories of the time Luis had brought her here. Horacio, it seemed, had a spare key, and once again Aunt Olga's flamboyant taste in colour hit her like the sun's sudden impact on weary eyes. Her eyes were not weary, but her heart was.

Again she was drawn to the view, the beauty of it tugging at her as forcibly as Luis's dark magnetism. Horacio asked, behind her,

'You like my nephew Luis's house, Katherine?'

'The house is wonderful,' she answered, after a long pause. 'It—it's what it represents that worries me.' There was another long silence, then she went on, 'Things like money, lots of it, an elegant, rich way of life.' Another pause. 'To me, it's wrong.' She turned to face Horacio. 'You see, my father has money, a great deal of it. I thought that was wrong, too, wrong because he never seems to have enough. He never stops working. All the time, his business comes first. It always has. He neglected my mother so much, she left him.'

Horacio nodded. 'But that does not mean Luis will neglect you,' he said gently.

'Oh, but you're wrong.' Katherine's eyes opened wider in an effort to convince. 'Luis brought me here. He said that soon I'd be moving in. When I asked what he would do, he said he'd stay at the hotel during the week, only coming here at weekends. What's that but neglecting me? I—I——' No, it was no use, she could not tell even Horacio how much she loved her husband.

'Come, let us sit down, Katherine.' His tone was kindly. 'These principles of yours. I think you are a little mixed up. You see, you are still looking at our way of living from the same point of view as you look at your own— and your countrymen's—way of living. Here, it is different. I think you need to know about Luis, his background, everything that made him the man he is.'

'I should like to know,' Katherine answered quietly. 'He's never told me.'

Horacio smiled. 'No, he would not because he would not see any reason why you should know. He has this arrogance, my nephew. In some, that is bad, but in him, it is a driving force. You see,' Horacio leaned forward, clasping his hands and looking at them, 'there is a tradition in this country that in order to live a decent life it is necessary to have the money to do it. What other way is there? You've seen our territory and how my countrymen make the very most of it.'

Katherine nodded eagerly. 'Not a single piece of land is neglected.'

'Even if it's on the edge of a precipice!' Horacio smiled. 'We work very hard here, Katherine. We must, otherwise we could not feed our families. We all work—the girls, the women, the boys, the fathers. Husbands go abroad to seek their fortunes.'

'You mean they emigrate?' Katherine asked, her eyes wide.

'For a few years. They go to South America, Australia, England, Europe, some to North America. As I said, we are used to working very hard, so when we go abroad, we work hard there, too. The husbands send back money to their wives and families. Also they save some. They get rich, in time, and return. They buy the land on which they and their families have worked—that is, if it belongs to a landlord. Or they buy more land. They have houses built.'

'Those houses I saw in the course of construction climbing the hills we passed yesterday?'

Horacio nodded. 'And they buy property.'

'I know Luis's father went abroad.'

'As you also know, he went to England.'

'Which is where he met Luis's mother.'

Horacio nodded. 'And where Luis was born. When

Pedro, Luis's father—also my brother—brought his English wife and little son back with him to Madeira, Pedro had made a great deal of money, enough, in fact, not only to start his export business——'

Katherine nodded. 'Luis has mentioned that.'

'But enough to have a very large hotel built.'

'The Hotel Sereno?'

Horacio nodded. 'He was not interested in running the hotel, so he leased the building to an overseas hotel company. When Luis's father died. Luis bought out the hotel and took over the running of it.'

'So now it all belongs to him?'

'And others in Europe and so on, including Lisbon, where he has gone this week. Pedro and I, and my brothers and sisters—they are spread around the world now—had a hard childhood. There were so many of us. Our mother worked night and day, tending the plot of land with our help, embroidering in the evenings—she was paid by a factory like so many women here—while our father was abroad.'

'He grew rich, too?'

Horacio shook his head. 'Those who failed were often too ashamed to return. So when tourists came, we boys asked them for money——'

Katherine nodded, remembering the numerous small boys who had clustered round her at times.

'We went to school and learned what we could. I went abroad, like our father, like Pedro. I, too, was successful. You have seen how I work and how I choose to live. I married, but my wife died a few years ago. Now I have only Jorge.' He smiled gently. 'Do you understand Luis a little better now?'

'Oh yes, yes. Thank you, Horacio, for telling me.'

'He works hard, Katherine, because it is in our blood. Also, if he did not, he would feel he was letting his late father down.'

'When he comes home, I'll tell him you've explained how it all came about, this wealth he has. And,' she coloured, looking away, 'I won't resent it any more.'

'Those principles of yours,' Horacio probed gently, 'they are appeased by what I have told you?'

Katherine smiled and nodded. 'Success when you have worked very hard for it isn't wrong. That much I've learnt.'

'And have you learnt to love your husband?'

'Oh, but I've loved him since the moment I met him!'

Horacio's head went back. 'I hope you have told him that?'

'Yes, many times.' She frowned. 'But I don't think he really believed me. It was the way it all started with us.'

Horacio rose. 'Let us go back to Funchal. All will be well between you, Katherine, I am certain of that.'

Katherine sighed. If only she could be as certain as Horacio. . . .

Three days had passed since Katherine's conversation with Horacio. She was looking forward eagerly to Luis's return. He had not contacted her. Even when she asked Jorge if he knew where Luis was, he shook his head.

Once Jorge saw her walking across the reception area with Dan, who had a few hours free. They were on their way to the swimming pool. Katherine wore her two-piece swimsuit under a button-through sundress, while Dan wore his shirt hanging loosely over his swimming trunks.

Katherine could see Jorge's taxi outside the front entrance and knew he had come to collect someone in answer to a call. Jorge did not smile at Katherine, but his disapproving look made her want to tell him there was nothing to be disapproving about. Couldn't he—couldn't anybody—understand that they were friends, just friends?

Next day Dan suggested that he might take her in his car to Monte for a ride on the toboggans. She agreed readily, finding the time hanging heavily and hoping the diversion would keep her mind from brooding on Luis's companion on his travels.

Were they, too, 'friends, just friends'? Having summed up Delphine's character, and remembering her more than friendly behaviour towards Luis when they met at the Country Club, she doubted it. The thought depressed her unduly.

Dan told her he would be free mid-morning. Selecting a dress from the collection which Luis had bought her— she winced as she remembered her lack of gratitude when they had been delivered—she fastened round her neck a gold chain bearing her initial. She had admired the pendant in the window of the hotel's jewellery shop while Dan was with her after swimming. He had immediately gone into the shop and bought it for her.

At first she had protested, saying that, as a married woman, she should not accept a gift from another man. He had laughed and said he was not 'another man', just one of her husband's employees, and anyway, it hadn't cost a fortune, had it, so what the hell?

Sensing a hint of hurt male pride, and remembering his thoughtfulness in giving the coach driver the tips the passengers had given to him she had accepted the gift with gratitude and a brief kiss on the cheek. Dan had coloured, the young woman behind the counter had smiled and lowered her eyes. It had not occurred to Katherine that she might have broken any rules in the Portuguese girl's eyes.

Her thoughts turned again to wondering when Luis would return. When he did, she would run into his arms. She would tell him that now Horacio had told her about his country's tradition of expecting the father of the family to work hard to achieve success, even going overseas, if necessary, as his father had done, she understood everything.

Nothing now would come between them and she would never leave him, never criticise him for the hours he worked because she knew why he was doing it—not just to add to his fortune, but to be able to pass it on to their children. And since she loved children, she didn't have any objection to. . . .

The telephone rang and Dan announced that he was waiting and when was she coming?

'Right now,' she answered, and hurried down to the reception area.

'It's a hired car,' Dan explained, leading her to the door after telling the girl in reception where he was going and that he'd be back for his usual painting session if anybody asked. 'I've had it since I came last March. I left my own back home at my parents' house, where I live.'

'Where's that?' Katherine asked as they made their way along the roads she was coming to know well.

'Not far from Miami, in Florida. But soon I'm going north, another state, maybe, get a place of my own.' He braked, saying, 'Here we are.'

Dan parked and they got out. He pointed to the long flight of steps leading to a church with twin towers. 'It's called Our Lady of the Mount Church,' he explained. 'Built in the eighteenth century on the remains of a fif-teenth-century chapel.'

There were villas and gardens and the air was fresh. Dan led Katherine to the start of the toboggan run and helped her into one of the 'toboggans'. These were like upholstered wicker chairs on runners. Two drivers appeared, wearing the traditional white uniforms, straw hats and rubber-soled boots.

The descent of the sledge was controlled by the drivers pulling or restraining the movement by ropes. Round the first bend a photographer was taking pictures. When one jumped quickly into the front of the sledge in which

Katherine sat with Dan, took a picture and jumped back, Dan said, 'Hope you smiled nicely for him. We get the pictures at the end of the run. They aren't free, by the way!'

'I never thought they were,' Katherine replied, laughing and enjoying the journey down to the bottom.

Dan helped her out of the sledge and as they stood gazing around, a photographer appeared carrying a pile of prints. Dan sorted through them, while Katherine looked over his shoulder, exclaiming, 'There it is!' when Dan came to it. He nodded to the man, asked the price and paid. Katherine tried to offer Dan the money, but he wouldn't take it.

'You have it this time,' said Dan. 'I'll have the one they take next time we come.'

Katherine held it to the light, inspecting it. From nowhere a voice said, 'There won't be a next time.'

The picture was snatched from her hand and she whirled round to see Luis, his face twisted with fury, staring at them. A few moments later the picture lay in shreds on the ground. 'You,' he said to Dan, 'you're fired. You,' he grasped Katherine's arm, 'come with me.'

Tugging free, she stared at him, ashen-faced. 'Dan's done nothing wrong. You can't fire him, you can't! All he's done is take me on the toboggan ride and pay for——'

'I can dismiss who the hell I like from my staff. As for you——'

'*Me*? I've done nothing wrong either. Don't judge me by the low standards you set yourself. Going away with a woman. . . .' Her lips trembled. Where was the dream of running into his waiting arms? 'I hate you, hate you!'

She turned and ran, making for the nearest taxi. Her voice was so full of tears, she had difficulty giving the driver the name of the hotel, but he seemed to understand. The moment they arrived, she paid him and raced for the entrance, for the first time failing to acknowledge the doorman's greeting.

The lift whisked her upwards and she entered the suite, slamming the door, locking it and leaning against it to get her breath. Finding a zipped shoulder bag, she thrust a few items into it, took out of a drawer the English money which she had carried with her on her journey there, and stuffed it into her purse. Taking a last look at Dan's painting of her, which she had hung in the sitting-room, she wondered bitterly if Luis would destroy that, too.

Down at reception, she asked the woman in charge if there was a plane due to leave for Britain that day. While the woman looked through the flight schedule, Katherine glanced constantly at the door, dreading Luis's appearance.

At last the woman said, 'No flight today to England, but one to Lisbon. From there you could take a plane to London.'

It was enough. Katherine thanked the woman and turned to go. 'What shall I tell Senhor de Freitas?' the woman called after her.

Katherine paused. 'Tell him goodbye. That's all,' she answered, and beckoned to the first in the line of taxis which were waiting outside.

On the journey across to Lisbon, where she took a plane for London, Katherine sat with a magazine on her lap. It remained unread. Her brain was too numb to function, even to take in simple sentences, even to think simple thoughts.

Eating sparingly, and scarcely conscious of her fellow passengers, she had her eyes closed for most of the time. Sleep did not come, although many of her companions slept soundly.

Arriving at last at Heathrow, weary of spirit, fighting fatigue, she telephoned her father's house. The voice that answered was Olga's. Inwardly, Katherine groaned. So she hadn't left yet for the Caribbean! The questions, as she had guessed, began at once.

'Is Luis with you? How are you both? How nice to see you again so soon. Yes, your father's here. Do you want us to send a car to collect the two of you?'

Katherine could not bring herself to tell her aunt that she was alone, that she had left Luis in Madeira. 'No car, thanks. I'll hire a taxi. See you soon, Aunt. Love to Dad.'

The front entrance door was opened as Katherine's hand lifted to the bell. Putting on a brave smile, she said, 'Hallo, Aunt——' She gasped. 'Mother!' Stepping inside, she put her baggage down and flung her arms round her mother's neck. 'Oh, Mum, it's so n-nice to see you.' Her body was shaking, but she couldn't help it.

Too many things had happened to her in the past few weeks, especially the past forty-eight hours, for her nervous system to have escaped disruption. She did not question why her mother was there. All she wanted to do was to cry her heart—and her problems—out, and that she certainly did.

Calmer at last, she seized a tissue from her pocket and scrubbed her face. She was conscious of her aunt hovering, of her father's voice inviting her in, but only when a few more minutes had elapsed and her mother's gentle smile turned questioning did Katherine feel able to cope with the rest of the family.

Olga, unrepentant in her choice of ostentatious clothes, stared horrified at her flushed face and dark shadows and asked, 'Where's my stepson?'

'She's left him,' her father joked, his round face flushed but happy, although Katherine could not think why. The sight of her own drooping figure would hardly inspire anyone to be cheerful.

'Yes, I have,' Katherine answered simply. 'It—it didn't work out.'

'What didn't work out?' Olga asked sharply.

'Our marriage, Aunt.'

'What nonsense, child! All marriages work out, if you're determined to make them.' She sat back in the chair. 'So my stepson isn't with you?'

Katherine shook her head. 'Dad, how are you? When we—I—saw you last, you were off work. Tired, you said.'

'Elspeth?' Halmar Matthews addressed his wife, inviting her to explain.

'Your father's got circulatory trouble, darling. Nothing serious, as long as he takes things more easily, takes his pills daily——'

'And has his wife by his side to care for him,' Halmar added, looking at Elspeth.

'And love him,' Elspeth added softly.

Katherine stared from one to the other. 'Wife? Love him? Mum, Dad—what have you been up to behind my back?' In spite of the mock suspicion in her tone, her eyes were brighter, more hopeful.

'He needed me, Kate,' Elspeth said, 'so I came.'

'You've married Dad again?' Her mother nodded. 'But do you love him?'

'I know what you're thinking. What about Ronald? Yes, I was very fond indeed of Ronald. But in a different way from your father.'

'He—he still works hard, Mum.'

'Did, Kate.' Halmar relaxed against the support of the armchair. 'I've retired now. Doctor's and——' he reached out for his wife's hand, 'your mother's orders.' They smiled fondly at each other.

Katherine could not miss the irony of the situation. In all of her actions, she had followed her mother—opting out from wealth, inadvertently marrying into it, resenting the devotion to his work of the man she married; finally, like her mother, leaving him.

Now here was she, contemplating ending her own marriage, while her mother had returned to the life partnership she had once turned her back on!

'I'm so pleased,' she exclaimed at last. 'You're both together again. And I've got my mother back! Thanks, Dad, thanks for——'

'Getting ill?' Halmar joked.

'No, no.' Katherine went to him and hugged him. 'For persuading a very important person to come back into our lives.'

As she resumed her seat, Aunt Olga commented, 'So here you are, in the bosom of your family, as they say, older and wiser, yet no happier. What went wrong?'

'A lot of things, Aunt. You see, Luis doesn't love me, never has. I don't know if he ever told you, but *I* proposed to *him*. I was foolish and impetuous and—sorry, Dad— thought I'd found a man who was different from all the others you tried persuading me to marry. This loan he said he wanted——'

Her father nodded, but Olga said sharply, 'Are you going to blame me for that piece of trickery? Because if you are, young woman, try including your father, who not only aided and abetted me, but suggested the whole thing.'

Sister glared at brother, who smiled, sought his wife's hand again and shrugged his shoulders. 'You told me Luis wanted a wife. I wanted a husband for my daughter. We both knew she'd refuse him if she knew the truth—that he was wealthy. So we thought of a scheme.'

'And I fell for it. Well,' Katherine interposed wearily, 'you may be surprised to hear that I did love Luis——'

'Did?' Olga exploded. 'Did? Don't you mean "do", young woman? No one who falls in love with my stepson falls *out* of love with him!'

'That's another matter, Aunt. Whether I do or not doesn't alter the fact that he's got another woman in his life.'

'Of course he had a woman in his life. He's quite

normal, not to mention virile, judging by the large number of female voices on the phone when I answered it at home.'

Halmar sighed. 'My sister never was noted for her tact, Kate.'

'It's all right, Dad.' She turned to Olga. 'I accept that, Aunt, but what I can't accept is the way he took this woman Delphine Evans with him the other day when he went to Lisbon. A business trip, he called it. I doubt if that's what she called it.'

Her listeners heard the waver in her voice and silence greeted her words.

'Well,' Olga glanced through the window to the road at the end of the long front garden, 'there's the taxi I called to take me to town.' She manoeuvred herself out of the chair and patted Katherine on the shoulder. 'Things will work out. Love will repair anything, even broken relationships. Look at your mother and father. They're together again.'

Katherine shook her head sadly. 'Thanks, Aunt Olga, but I told you, Luis doesn't love me. He told me he only married me to have a permanent woman in his life.'

Olga patted her again, said goodbye to her brother and sister-in-law and swept out of the house. Elspeth looked at the clock on the bookcase.

'Time for your rest, dear,' she said to her husband. He nodded and heaved himself upright. Katherine noticed that he had lost weight which, she reasoned, remembering the extra inches he had carried around, was a good thing.

Alone, Katherine felt the silence weigh heavily. Wandering to the window, she stared out at the rose-filled garden and wondered where her own future lay. Two years separation, followed by divorce. Find a job, nine-to-five routine, maybe a boy-friend or two, but no close relationship—after Luis's lovemaking, the thought of allowing another man to touch her was repugnant.

Anyway, she loved him, always would. With another sigh she went into the entrance hall for her shoulder bag. It was essential to stop thinking, since her thoughts were going round in circles. Slowly she climbed the stairs to her old room.

There was a sound of footsteps following. Aunt Olga? But she had gone out. Turning, she saw a man, brown-eyed dark-haired, body lean, shoulders broad, and her heart pounded like a hammer. He reached upward to take her bag, but she wrenched it from him, raced to her room, closed the door—but there was no lock. Against his strength, her slender shoulders didn't stand a chance.

He was in the room, back to the door, eyes as icy as they had been when he had ripped the photograph to pieces.

'How did you get here?' she whispered, her face as white as if his cold gaze had inflicted frostbite.

'By plane. How else.'

'Via Lisbon, like me?'

'My own private aircraft from Madeira. Yes, I have one, although I didn't tell you, knowing of your *very strict* principles.' His tone grazed her sensibilities.

A suspicion entered her mind. 'Does the family know you're here?'

'Of course. When you arrived I was in the next room, which meant I heard your outpourings.'

So once again they had tricked her! 'If I'd known I was being overheard, I'd have been even more outspoken,' she snapped.

'That would have been difficult,' he responded dryly. 'So my business trip was merely a smoke screen, was it, to cover my real objective—of taking a short vacation with Delphine Evans, who you had the impudence to imply was my mistress? Yet while I was away, you spent every spare moment with Dan Stewart, letting him kiss you, embrace you——'

'We did not kiss,' she stormed, her anger getting the better of her, 'except for that evening when the folk dancers came to the restaurant and you were watching us. Nor did we embrace, unless you call Dan's arm round my shoulders embracing?'

His head was back, his hands in his pockets. His half-hooded eyes lingered on her throat. 'That pendant—I've never seen it before. Is it gold?'

'Yes. It's new, too. Dan bought it for me from the hotel jewellery shop, as you probably know, having no doubt scoured the hotel, not to mention Funchal itself, for clues to my unfaithfulness. I told Dan I couldn't accept the pendant, but he insisted, so instead of hurting his pride, I took it. And kissed *his cheek*.'

'In payment,' Luis sneered, 'for——'

'Don't you dare finish that sentence, don't you dare!' Her eyes blazed at him. 'Will you get out of my room and take your insults with you?' He did not move. 'All right, you stay, I'll go.' She had almost reached the door when his hand caught her wrist. He swung her round.

'You're staying.' His arms went round her and his fingers fastened on to the back of her head. His mouth descended, his hard lips fought with hers, finally winning the battle by forcing her lips to part under his.

There was the taste of him again, mixing with hers. The chemistry reacted as it always had, one with the other, creating a combustible substance which exploded into a miniature eruption. It lifted them high on a shining cloud, leaving Katherine treading air and clinging to his strong, hard body in case she fell off the edge into an empty nothingness . . . which was the state in which she existed when the man she loved was not there any more.

Breathless once he had let her mouth go, she said, 'No, no, this is all wrong. We're separated. That's why I left you——'

'Separated? Left me?' His jaw grew rigid, his brown

eyes glittered like hard-packed snow. 'I'll demonstrate just how *separate* we are!' He lifted her, carrying her to the bed. His practised hands soon disposed of all her covering, taking only a few moments to repeat the process with himself.

The familiar and potent feel of his body against hers, his desire making his demands insistent and relentless, his mouth burning a fiery trail all over her, carried her back to that cloud.

The feel of his arousing lips on her breasts, her throat and finally her mouth again, the urgency of his need for her, his driving determination to make her one with him, to demonstrate that she was nothing without him, had her yielding to his every wish.

She did everything in her power to please him, to obey his harsh commands, and when at last the moment of greatest ecstasy came, it was as if she were blinded by a golden aura above the cloud, and she closed her eyes to keep in the joy lest it escape for ever.

For a while they lay, totally at peace, Luis's arms still imprisoning her. His head lifted at last. There was a gleam in his eyes, of triumph—and something else. The ice had melted. 'Leave me? Never!' he said. 'I've told you before. I'd pursue you to the ends of the earth and back, no matter how many golden pendants you might have collected from other men on the way.'

Katherine fingered the pendant. 'Luis, oh, Luis,' she murmured, and folded into him. 'This pendant—it means nothing, except a sign of friendship. Dan was honest, warm-hearted, straighforward.'

Luis's eyebrow rose. 'Everything, in fact, which I'm not?'

Katherine reached for a cover and drew it over them. 'At least he wouldn't have done what you did.'

'What did I do?' he asked, menace in his gaze, anger in his voice.

'You fired him, for nothing! For stopping me from being lonely, for taking me with the hotel guests on a coach tour of the island, for taking me on that toboggan ride. We did nothing, nothing of which either of us should be ashamed.'

'I heard differently from Jorge.'

'Jorge's a nice young man and I like him, but he was misreading the situation, like you did. Despite—everything, I'll never forgive you for firing Dan.'

'I suppose it offended those principles of yours?'

'Stop talking so contemptuously of my principles!' His answer was to run a finger over her eyebrows. 'Luis——'

'Mm?' His finger was busy moving downwards from her throat.

'I had a talk with Horacio.' He was making it difficult for her to concentrate. 'He told me about——' How could she find the right words, especially as his lips had taken the place of his finger. 'About how the Madeiran people believe in hard work, how the men go abroad, working all hours, send back money to their families. . . . Will you listen to me?' she added desperately, gripping his hair and pulling.

In return, he gripped her wrist, but his head found the pillow again, his eyes patient. There was emotion in her eyes as they sought his. 'I know now how hard your father worked over here in Britain, how he married here and you were born here, and still your father went on working. Then, when he had made enough money, he took you and your mother to Madeira and started a business, even buying . . .'

'Well,' his face was enigmatic now, 'you know it all.'

'Now I know it all. But it's too late.'

His anger surfaced again. 'Too late for what?'

'Well, I—I love you, Luis, but I just can't respect you any more. You see, you sacked a man from his job when he did nothing wrong.'

Luis grasped her chin, his fingers bruising. 'Carry on,' he ordered, threatening now.

She went on huskily, 'Once Horacio had told me everything about you, I was so pleased, I realised that working hard like you did, like your father did, earning money through effort and sheer determination, was not against my principles.'

'Do go on, my own,' he encouraged silkily.

Katherine distrusted his smile, which was suave and sardonic. Nevertheless she persisted. 'I had it all planned in my mind. The moment I saw you when you'd returned, I was going to run into your arms and tell you,' she paused, noticing that his smile was fading, 'tell you I understood. I was going to say I would work with you, helping you wherever I could, for the sake of—of the sons and daughters we would have one day.' Her eyes grew moist at the memory of their meeting, shattering the dream. 'Then,' despairing eyes found his, 'you tore up that picture and sacked Dan. So it's too late.'

'If I told you that when I'd heard Dan's explanation I withdrew my dismissal? Would it still be too late?'

'You did?' Katherine had the strangest feeling he was laughing at her.

'I did.'

'So he's still an employee?'

'He is. And if I told you that when I returned to Madeira and found you were out with Dan Stewart, I drove like a madman to the foot of the toboggan run feeling murderous because I thought he'd become your lover? And if I told you that, instead of tearing you apart, which was my instinct, I tore that picture instead, and fired the man beside you? And,' he moved into closer contact again, 'if I told you I was in such a jealous rage that if I'd dragged you back to the hotel and had my way with you, you'd have hated me for the rest of your life?'

Katherine's fingers dug into the muscles of his forearms.

'But there was Delphine—you took her to Lisbon with you.'

'Let's get it right, shall we, my love?' he replied abruptly. 'She accompanied me on the journey. As I said, she went on business, like me.'

'She loves you, Luis. I heard her tell you.'

'If she loves me, that is her misfortune. She means nothing to me. There's only one woman in the world that I love, and that, my darling, is you.'

'You—you mean you really love me?'

'Love you? Didn't you know? Hadn't you guessed? I've loved you since before I met you. Your father showed me ciné-film of you taken at home, on holiday, with various male hangers-on. I hated them and fell headlong for you. Why else do you think I agreed to their suggestion about posing as a man in need of money? Why else did I accept your proposal of marriage?'

'You turned it down,' she retorted indignantly.

'Only so that I could do the thing properly and propose to *you*.'

'So, right from the start, the cards were stacked against me.'

'You couldn't win, my love.' His smile grew reflective, gratified. 'I had you here in the palm of my hand.' His voice lowered, his eyes grew lazy, scanning her curving form possessively. 'Just as I have you now, here in my arms. And here you'll stay, *querida*, night after night. For ever.'

Mills & Boon
Best Seller Romances

The very best of Mills & Boon Romances
brought back for those of you who missed
them when they were first published.
In December
we bring back the following four
great romantic titles.

LAND OF ENCHANTMENT
by Janet Dailey

Diana was a city girl, a glamorous model; Lije Masters was a tough
rancher from New Mexico. But they met, fell in love, and were
married – just like that. Would Diana now find herself 'repenting
at leisure'?

UNWARY HEART
by Anne Hampson

For her family's sake, Muriel had to find a rich husband – and she
fixed on Andrew Burke as the 'lucky man'. But Andrew was one
jump ahead of her – or was he?

COME THE VINTAGE
by Anne Mather

Ryan's father had left her a half share of his prosperous
vine-growing business, and the other half to a man she had never
heard of, a Frenchman named Alain de Beaunes – on condition that
they married each other. So, for the sake of the business, they
married, neither caring anything for the other. Where did they go
from there?

COURT OF THE VEILS
by Violet Winspear

'In many respects the desert is like a woman. Anything might crop
up in the desert, as in a relationship with a woman . . . But a man
can enjoy the desert without getting involved – emotionally.'
Duane Hunter's words made it quite plain to Roslyn that there
was no future for her in his life. And yet . .

If you have difficulty in obtaining any of these books through your
local paperback retailer, write to:

Mills & Boon Reader Service
P.O. Box 236, Thornton Road, Croydon, Surrey, CR9 3RU

How to join in a whole new world of romance

It's very easy to subscribe to the Mills & Boon Reader Service. As a regular reader, you can enjoy a whole range of special benefits. Bargain offers. Big cash savings. Your own free Reader Service newsletter, packed with knitting patterns, recipes, competitions, and exclusive book offers.

We send you the very latest titles each month, postage and packing free – no hidden extra charges. There's absolutely no commitment – you receive books for only as long as you want.

We'll send you details. Simply send the coupon – or drop us a line for details about the Mills & Boon Reader Service Subscription Scheme.
Post to: Mills & Boon Reader Service, P.O. Box 236, Thornton Road, Croydon, Surrey CR9 3RU, England.
*Please note: READERS IN SOUTH AFRICA please write to: Mills & Boon Reader Service of Southern Africa, Private Bag X3010, Randburg 2125, S. Africa.

Please send me details of the Mills & Boon Subscription Scheme.
NAME (Mrs/Miss) _____ EP3
ADDRESS _____
_____

COUNTY/COUNTRY_____ POST/ZIP CODE _____
BLOCK LETTERS, PLEASE

ills & Boon
 of romance